MW00648570

ADVANCE PRAISE FOR *Words Made Flesh*

"Patricia Lynn Reilly's stories and poems speak poignantly to the child in all of us, the frightened and resourceful survivor who creates herself anew with words."
>   —ALISON LUTERMAN, Poet, playwright, and author of
>   *The Largest Possible Life*

"Touching hearts with wonder and hope, Patricia Lynn Reilly's lyrical wisdom is a boon to those who wish to think, grow, and heal. A must read for both the orphaned and angelic voices within our souls."
>   —SUE PATTON THOELE, Author of *The Courage To Be Yourself*
>   and *Growing Hope*

"Patricia Lynn Reilly has lived a life worth sharing. *Words Made Flesh* reveals her courage and strength in handling life's unfolding with grace. The beauty of Patricia's feminist thought and expression make this a wonderful book for meditation and inspiration."
>   —ARLENE GOETZ, Publisher of the Catholic Women's Network

"*Words Made Flesh* refreshes, challenges, delights, and liberates! Patricia Lynn Reilly is fully embodied in her words. They are strong, searing in their truthfulness, a joy to read. They remind us all, women and men alike, that nothing is wrong with us, that life is here and now, and that the kiss-friendly spirit of life sustains us always. Allow Patricia's words to call forth in you what is good, beautiful, and true."
>   —JAMES WELLMAN, Ph.D., Assistant Professor of Western
>   Religions, Jackson School of International Studies, University
>   of Washington, and author of *The Gold Coast and the Ghetto:
>   Christ and Culture in Mainline Protestantism*

ADVANCE PRAISE FOR *Words Made Flesh*

"This is a book for those who dare to imagine their way into that large and dangerous and unsettling and wondrous world of Art and Spirit. It is a testimony for those who seek to enter into the deeper truths of imagination than those marketed for cheap public consumption. It is a record of one woman's journeying through the darkness toward the light, where pain and healing and struggle and hope are not easily disentangled. Call it a witness to the intensities of Spirit. Call it the journal of an audacious pilgrim committed to the artist's way. This is not a book for the timid of heart, or the conventional of mind. It is a risky book embodying what one writer has called the 'warnings and chances and painful beauty' of art. Take it and read, if you have the audacity to imagine engaging the visionary path of change."

—**MARK S. BURROWS**, Ph.D., Professor of History and Faculty Director of the Arts and Theology Program, Andover Newton Theological School, Newton Centre, MA, and author of the forthcoming *Bernard of Clairvaux, The Triumph of Desire*

Words Made Flesh

Patricia Lynn Reilly

ALSO BY PATRICIA LYNN REILLY, M.DIV.

A God Who Looks Like Me (BALLANTINE BOOKS, 1995)
Be Full of Yourself! (OPEN WINDOW CREATIONS, 1998)
Imagine a Woman in Love with Herself (CONARI PRESS, 1999)
I Promise Myself (CONARI PRESS, 2000)

WORDS MADE *flesh*

An anthology of writings by

PATRICIA LYNN REILLY

Foreword by
Fran Grace, Ph.D.

OPEN WINDOW CREATIONS ∴ CALIFORNIA

© 2004 BY PATRICIA LYNN REILLY

Published by Open Window Creations
P. O. Box 8615, Berkeley, California 94707

All Rights Reserved. No part of this publication may be reproduced in any manner whatsoever without written permission from Open Window Creations, except in the case of brief quotations in reviews.

ISBN: 0-9661642-1-0

Cover Concept: Patricia Lynn Reilly
Cover and Book Design: Courtnay Perry
Printed in the United States of America

Copies may be ordered from:
Open Window Creations
P. O. Box 8615
Berkeley, California 94707
www.openwindowcreations.com
See appendix for companion resources.

·:· **CONTENTS**

Reversals

∴ **FOREWORD**
by Fran Grace, Ph.D.,
author of *Carry A. Nation: Retelling the Life*

The arrival into the world of *Words Made Flesh* makes me want to beat
my drum, shake a tambourine in each hand, and dance with my arms
stretched high in a circle of joyous and laughing friends!

I read Patricia's first book, *A God Who Looks Like Me*, with a flash-
light under my sheets, trembling with excitement and fear. I relished
the impulses and truths that Patricia's retelling of biblical stories awakened in me, but I feared the punishing judgments of my then-hus-
band and all the patriarchs he represented to me. I dreaded the cocked
eyebrow, the rolling eyes, the turned back, the strike of lightning from
father god. But I couldn't stop reading either!

The stories of Lilith, Mary, and the One Who Shed Her Blood
guided me to see my religious background with a new set of eyes.
These eyes actively sought out images, experiences, people, and words
that affirmed my essential woman-goodness. Ah! What a sweet
moment when I began to embrace my strength rather than suppress
it! And the voices of contemporary women in *A God Who Looks Like
Me* connected me to my own questions, longings, and feelings. I took
refuge from my loneliness in their expressions of anger, loss, and fear.
Whatever was happening to me, their voices assured me, I was not
alone.

In *Words Made Flesh*, Patricia continues the brave acts of gathering fragments and naming truths. This time, however, the fragments
are not only those of voiceless women like Mary and Eve, but also

included are the fragments of Patricia's own forgotten childhood. And the truths are not only those drawn from circles of women, but also the truths of Patricia's fiercely conscious engagement with her own life. She unwraps each story, poem, and meditation as if it were a gorgeous package—a gift from life itself to teach the lessons of letting go, trusting her intuitive impulses, staying present, participating fully in both joy and pain, dancing her feelings, enduring violence and desertion, and loving her body. "Hold onto nothing. Participate in everything."

Patricia's gifts to the world have always been grounded in the personal mind-body-heart experiences of real women. But *Words Made Flesh* offers a deep and generous encounter with Patricia herself as she harvests and nurtures from her own difficult life the seeds of self-trust, acceptance, and grace. These are the stories and poems of a woman who relentlessly celebrates her body's desires, who refuses to numb herself to pain or death, who speaks her truth. Encountering Patricia in *Words Made Flesh* is to encounter the "I" in Jennifer Welwood's poem, "Unconditional":

> *Opening to my loss,*
> *I gain the embrace of the universe.*

Thank you, Patricia. Again.

∴ FRAGMENTS OF THE FORGOTTEN

Private Words

I love words. Words becoming flesh and feeling, sweat and sensation. Words teasing, arousing, and moistening. Words opening mind, body, and memory. Words stimulating thought, inspiring action, changing lives. Words clarifying what's in, under, and around them. I like clarity, too. I don't like obscuration. I consider it a compliment when someone understands my words, when they say the meaning is apparent, not layered, not hidden, not requiring pursuit.

I've been writing simple, clear words since I was seven. Gathering my feeling, longing, and tears into words to my father 3,000 miles away. "I miss you, Daddy." Letters found tied with a ribbon in his lonely apartment after his death. Letters to my Nana and Mama while in the orphanage, reaching out to touch and remember them through words. Words written with my tears, received by theirs. Words, ever hopeful of reunion. Shared tears. Shared hope. Words becoming flesh, the tie that binds, across the excruciating distance.

In high school I wrote letters to God every day—my responses to daily Bible readings. My words, longing for God to approve my choices, my beliefs, my zeal. "Father in heaven, hear my prayer, make me perfect, use me to change the world." God became flesh, they say. The Word became flesh and dwelt among us. That which was indiscernible, out of reach, beyond pursuit, was born of flesh to become flesh. From abstraction to fleshiness. From platforms and positions to vulnerability. From word to touch to sacred messiness, to life here and now, till death do us part.

At college New Testament words circumscribed my intellectual pursuits and vocational interests: "Suffer not a woman to teach, not to usurp authority over the man. For Adam was formed first, then Eve." I was an anomaly, at the top of my class in an institution that denied full professorships to women. Men were the leaders and teachers. Women were the followers and students. No matter how successful I was, I remained ineligible to become a minister, theologian, or professor—the vocations for which I had been unintentionally groomed since childhood. Like the steady drip of an IV inserted at birth, my dreams were silenced by the words absorbed into my life stream.

The Bible I read daily as a child, adolescent, and young adult was filled with men's words, stories, and interpretations of the divine. Two impulses arose within me during those years. The vulnerability of my status as orphan required that I learn the party line and conform to it. Yet a deeper part of my being remained untouched by those words. That part was accumulating courage for the day when I would leave the suffocating world of fundamentalism and venture into the open spaces of a life-affirming spirituality. This little light of mine, I'm going to let it shine. Won't let anyone blow it out!

After college, I began to question God's words in the secret of my heart. They were harsh and restrictive. They denied the good within and around me. They divided the world into simplistic categories: good/bad; god/devil; believer/unbeliever; heaven/hell. I longed for words of welcome and celebration rather than words of warning and judgment. I longed for spaciousness, for more room around my thoughts and feelings, for deeper breaths, for playmates beyond the chosen, the elect, the predestined. An open window. Blow, fresh air, blow into dusty rooms of old. Refresh and make new.

My secret courage was nourished as I gathered an alternative scripture from the works of poets, artists, and writers. Given my early identification with men, Walt Whitman, Rainier Rilke, Chaim Potok, and Hermann Hesse were the first to feed my suspicion of the "Word of God." Unlike the rigid teachings of my childhood and adolescence, which imprisoned the divine and prescribed my responses, the life-affirming visions of these men employed open language and unfolding imagery. Their words deepened my longing to venture out beyond orthodoxy; their images inspired my imagination.

I read Walt Whitman's *Leaves of Grass* in a secret corner of the Princeton Seminary library. I drank in his blasphemous words. They quenched my lifelong thirst for a language with which to celebrate myself without conditions, apologies, or disclaimers. Having just begun the journey through my intellectual, religious, and personal past, I wasn't ready to allow his words to form on my lips, yet they remained within me and inspired my journey. Years later, my three-fold journey completed, Whitman's words from "Song of Myself" became my first self-celebration. I am larger, better than I thought. I did not know I held so much goodness.

Studying at the Women's Theological Center, I assumed intellectual and theological equality with the gods of traditional religion and Western civilization and their sacred text, the Bible. The dethronement of the male God was a crucial task to complete on my journey. My imagination, intellect, and vision were freed of the shackles of a lifetime as his words and images were exorcised from my mind, heart, and body. To know anything at all about our history, our bodies, ourselves, we must reach beyond what they told us, what they taught us, what they want from us. We must reach back to the very beginning.

Grounded in my own life, supported by a circle of women, I concentrated on two areas of professional development during the early '90s. Determined to give as many hours of attention, creativity, and support to women as I had given to men, I developed my ministry among women and designed a business capable of holding the full range of my creative adventures. Determined to write as many words in service of my own professional life as I had written to the men and gods whose swirls inspired hundreds of pages of prayers, poems, exhortations, sermons, and manipulations, I outlined several writing projects, secured an agent, and sold my first book to a publisher. Since then I have written three more books. I imagine them as my daughters, born of the vow of faithfulness to myself.

Public Words

As an author I have never begun a project with a blank page. In my experience writing is more like gathering words, regularly turning toward them, and then crafting them to reach beyond, beneath, in back of themselves. Each idea, outline, and assignment begins with a ritual reading of my journals and writings for inspiration, for the kernel that will eventually become the chapter, article, keynote address, lecture, performance piece, or book. As the words travel from my journal (private musings rooted in the fleshiness of my tears, sweat, longing, arousal, and fear) to book, article, and lecture (public declarations crafted for an audience), they are often drained of their personal vulnerability, of the messiness of ordinary life that gave birth to them in the first place.

Yet underneath the public words, the private fleshiness pulsates: there she is, *the abandoned girl*, longing for her mother, heard in the reworked prayers of the feminist theologian: "Our Mother, who art within us;" *the fearful girl*, befriending the darkness of solitary confinement, heard in the priestess' tribute to Mother Darkness; *the fierce adolescent*, wrestling for her place as world-changer among the boys, heard in the iconoclast's challenge: "God the father has remained an undisturbed idol for too long;" and *the troubled young woman*, struggling to love her body, to come out of hiding, heard in the words of the WomanChurch minister: "It is right and good that you are woman." Listen deeply enough to any author's words and you will touch their personal vulnerability.

Once tossed to the winds as public writings, many of the selections you'll read in this anthology have developed a life of their own. Some are used by others in their dissertations, published books, magazines, newsletters, web postings, and course readers. They are quoted by kindred spirits—words from *Imagine a Woman in Love With Herself* quoted by the founder of Femail Creations as her inspiration for dreaming big, and by angry detractors—words from *A God Who Looks Like Me* used as evidence that the Teletubbies are part of a godless conspiracy. Some of the selections you'll read have lived quieter lives, remaining on the pages of my journal until now. In the fullness of time, musing becomes word becomes journal entry becomes public expression becomes flesh again in the experience of you, the reader.

My male friends have asked, "When are you going to give birth to a son?" *Words Made Flesh* is a love-*child*, born of the trouble and beauty, gift and challenge of my own life. It is a collection of my poetry and prose gathered from my journals, letters, poems, sermons, lectures, presentations, performance pieces, project proposals, articles, ceremonies, songs, and books. It will take you on a journey through the first half of my life. Even when my words are addressed to a couple, an audience, a congregation, a publisher, or a class, they tell my story. Listen in the spaces between and around and within the words, and you will hear my childhood longings. Nothing has been lost or forgotten. In the roundabout way life works, all is re-membered, re-surrected, re-constituted, redemptively re-enacted.

Elevate not the beginning. Despise not the ending.
All is seasonal, not harsh.
Honor coming and going, holding on and letting go,
joy and sorrow, reunion and separation.

Hold onto nothing. Participate in everything.
Notice all that is and bless it, as it shifts and changes in a moment.
A full emptiness, unfolding from the center—
always new, always now, always and not yet, always and never.

Beginnings

Comings and Goings

I have a friend. The comings and goings of those she loved into and out of her life began very early. Her father was an alcoholic. He was home for a few days, then gone for a few, a coming always followed by a going. She experienced moments of beauty when he was present. He would give "his girl" gifts of silver dollars and chocolate milk. Her heart would soar, but he would always leave again. She made up stories, as any four- or five-year-old would, to make sense of his comings and goings. *He comes when I'm good. He leaves when I'm bad.* Stories to make sense of life. One day he left for good.

My friend and her mother survived together for a year or two after the divorce, but the pressures of life plunged the mother into her own alcoholism. One day her mother disappeared, and the little girl, my friend, was taken to an orphanage in a station wagon driven by strangers. During her five years there, she created one story after another to make sense of her mother's disappearance. The little girl was sure her mother was dead.

And then on the day of her eighth grade graduation, her mother came again. The little girl, now twelve, didn't recognize her mother for a moment; she had been dead for five years. The little girl had worked out the good-byes; they seemed to last forever. The hellos took another lifetime to accept.

Circling the Planets

A scream lived in a little girl's heart.

Just say good morning and good night.
No other exchanges are acceptable.
Be sure the image is protected, kept securely in its place.
Don't assault it with your feelings.
Don't challenge it with your needs.
Don't question it with your individuality.

No loud noises, no strange movements.
No bright colors, no humming.
There's a string on your shoulder.
There's blood on your sheet.
It's your fault. Your body's fault.
Your mother's fault.

Waking up in a strange place surrounded by veiled women.
Just say good morning and good night.
Nice neat cottages, everything in its place.
Just say good morning and good night.
It's a concentration camp, for god's sake.
Just say good morning and good night.

Keep the image intact, abandoned.
Keep the image intact, an orphanage.
Keep the image intact, a storeroom of shadows.

You are a bad girl.
You were scared and you shook.
You were hurt and you said so.
You were and they wouldn't let you be.

The scream grew bigger as they twisted her goodness into evil. It grew louder as they twisted her strength into weakness. It grew stronger as they twisted her truth into lies.

The scream filled her body, and found voice in seizures, erupting from the depths of the scream. It filled her life, and found voice in the aching present, twisted into the shapes of the past. It filled her heart, and there was no room for love.

One day, Gentle Love—in the shape of a light blue chair with a big lap just like her grandma's—approached the little girl. Her body shook. Her life twisted. Her heart ached. Gentle Love came close enough to hear the scream. *I will not hurt you,* Gentle Love said. *Please do not twist me into the shapes of the past. Allow me to live freely. Allow me to grow within you.*

Gentle Love's words set free the scream. It erupted in blood and darkness. It circled the planets, shouting in the open spaces of the universe. It splashed across the sky as sparkling fireworks brightening the darkness. The little girl rode on the back of the scream as it danced, and circled, and splashed.

Gentle Love called to her, *Come to the clearing. Sit down and rest, and your scream is welcome too.* So the little girl, holding her tired scream, rested in the clearing. She was thirsty. As she drank of the golden green-blue stream surrounding the clearing, she swallowed the scream and it settled within her peacefully. Gentle Love found a home too, within the little girl's heart, for now there was room.

Chosen Families

There were times when my childhood imagination soared as I imagined another childhood—one with loving parents. While in St. Joseph's Village, an institution for dependent children, I became a popular tour guide on weekend afternoons. Kind-hearted Catholic families from northern New Jersey stopped by to tour the spacious complex and to meet the "orphans."

Besides making lots of money, prompting the nuns to institute a restriction on the amount I could keep, I was examining each family for new qualities to add to my "loving family" fantasy. I watched the way the parents looked at their children: Were their eyes filled with gentleness or harshness? I listened to the tone of voice they used in conversation with their children: Were their voices patient or irritable? I paid special attention to how they touched their children: Were the exchanges affectionate or rough?

By the end of an afternoon, I knew who the kindest families were and hoped they would ask for permission to take me home for a weekend...or a lifetime. And most of them did ask. I spent many weekends with kind families who nourished my imaginative fantasies of the family I wanted—one that kept its children.

Throughout my life, I have adopted families, chosen families, who have looked at me with gentleness, who have spoken to me with respect, and who have touched me with affection. One by one, I have "imagined into being" the powerful visions I developed in reaction and response to childhood realities.

Contrasting Visions

The Catholic Mary
I could not see the Queen of Heaven's body
through her clothes.
I wonder, What was she hiding
beneath those floor length robes:
her breasts and pubic hair?
Perhaps the Queen of Heaven has no body
like the paintings and statues fashioned in her image,
were her robes painted atop a blank canvas
or chiseled into an absent body?

The Queen of Heaven was stripped of her earthiness.
She answered my prayers
yet she could not tell me how it felt
to join my body with another.
What else could one expect?
She lived in the heavens with the men
a neuter, untouchable and untouched.

The Protestant Mary
The Sunday School Mary had a body,
a young woman's soft and lovely body.
Overshadowed by the power of the Most High,
no loving arms attended her opening.
The pregnant Mary,
her belly and breasts growing in fullness,
spilling over with the life of god.

The Mary of Earth had a body, yet it wasn't hers,
god could do whatever he wanted to it.
Stripped of her will, kept in her place
quietly surrendering to those who know best,

she accepted her role as mother,
only a mother, to the exclusion of all else,
to the denial of her own life.
Where was her voice? Did she ever say, "No More"?

All Is Not as It Seems
I imagine the Mary of Earth confused, troubled, and angry
within the secrecy of her heart, where no man could hear her.
Mary, reclaiming her will, daring to question
the outrageous, the disruptive, and the inhumane.
Mary, reclaiming her voice, shouting, "No More."

If the Mary of Earth discovered a place to assert her will
to question the dictates of gods and men,
I wonder, did the Queen of Heaven
have a place to own her body? Did she masturbate?
Was her place of rebellion in the darkness of the night
where she could not be reached by definitions
imposed by priests and kings?
Was her bed a virgin bed in which she nightly
shed her robes and savored her woman-body,
"This is *my* body. I will take and eat."

Telling the Untold Stories

While gathering the fragments of my own forgotten childhood, I encountered stories from my religious past that startled me. They were terrible stories of nameless and voiceless women, of women whose stories I was not told in the churches of my childhood and adolescence. These stories were passed over in Sunday school and seldom mentioned from the pulpit.

The stories of King David's conquests were well known, yet no mention was made of his daughter Tamar, who was raped by Amnon her brother. I was taught in exacting detail about the adventures of kings and priests. Yet the abusive treatment of their unnamed wives and concubines was seldom given any attention except in passing as supporting detail. And no one, in either the Bible text or in the pulpit, expressed outrage at the treatment of the women in these tragic stories.

Yet, the churches of my childhood included a regular ritual in which we honored the broken body and the shed blood of Jesus Christ. A wounded male was honored, his broken body ritualized. Wounded women went unnamed, their broken bodies brutalized in the silence.

The Power of the Most High

Arriving early to a healing retreat, I sat on the church steps facing a statue of Mary. The words from Luke 1:34 flooded my heart: "The Holy Spirit will come upon you and the power of the Most High will overshadow you." *Oh my god*, I exclaimed aloud, *Mary was raped!* In that moment I understood her silence, her distance, her robes. I wrote to her.

Mary, raped by god
you know the terror and the shame
your life disrupted
your body torn open
by the shadow of the most high
a crime committed in the name of the lord.

Mary, handmaiden of patriarchy
forced to do its bidding—

No more dark shadows
overtaking us in the night.

No more silent penetrations
ripping us open and apart.

No more ice-cold loneliness
enfolding us in our wet and empty beds.

The sin is yours, father god.
We will no longer carry its weight
within our bodies, atop our lives.

No More!

Night Vision

Night is a place, beyond time.
To enter you must have night vision.
The capacity to see what others don't.
Did you eat your carrots?

The Station Wagon With Wood Panels
takes you there, no words are spoken;
before you know it, you've arrived.
The ladies in white are muzzled by the night.
They can't touch you when the lights are out;
they're afraid of the dark.

The Curlitopped Twins
play with fire while no one is watching.
They are alone, always alone in the night.
Their fear turns to fire before your eyes
and nothing is left of the day's terror.
It disappears in the night flames.

The Old Man of the Corridor
follows you everywhere; he says you steal everything.
The old woman, his wife, lives in a storeroom
with twenty wedding dresses, trench coats, and knives,
bought at midnight in Filene's basement.
In the dark she gives you twenty-dollar bills and scarves.

The Mama Who Forgets
during the day when its hard not to,
remembers moment by moment in the night.
You visit her in the sitting room
where she shows her polka-dot paintings,
the same images over and over again
yet her stories are always new.

Mary, the Homeless One
gives lessons in daytime survival:
Pretend to be plural during the day,
when uniformity is required for safety.
Return to the singular only at night,
a reunion with the edges of your solitude.

The Silver Cart
with a cow on the platter
and unnamed gifts from the sea,
moves on its own, slowly down the long corridor,
stopping to feed the children.
Only in the night, undetected,
do they dare eat from the silver cart.

The Veiled Woman
appears in the floor hourly
and the earth shakes.
Ten crystals drop at each sighting,
scattering into the corners.
One for each year you wandered in the desert.

Marie, the Choreographer
teaches you to dance in the middle of the night
where the definitions of the day cannot reach you,
where you become Mame, Fred Astaire, and Cleopatra.
A pretty girl with a melody, all around the town,
in the night place, in the magic space, beyond their expectations.

Leo, the Fat Woman
makes you laugh until you cry.
Her terrorizing awakens
the gargoyles in your soul.
She exiles you to the storeroom,
where the darkness is your friend.

On a sliver of light she returns
and you wish again for the dark.

The Artist from Turkey
signs in for a short stay.
You sit for him in the night.
He paints your picture with an O'Keeffe sky
and asks why your dreams never mention your name;
a distance preserved in fantasy and grace.

The Silver Dollars
are stored away someplace in the Night.
Had to leave them in a hurry a long time ago.
Tonight, you will find them
when the guardians of the light fall asleep,
when silver treasures return
as homing pigeons to their original owners.

Mocha Pearl
shows her jewels,
glistening from her belly button.
Gathered during the day,
in places unsuspected,
she shows them in the corners
and they glisten our way through the night.

Seamstress Jane
makes costumes in her closet,
where she fulfills your secret dreams.
A boy in the day, wrapped in a suit.
In Jane's dark closet, you wear a dress.
Now father won't touch you; he doesn't like girls.
A girl in the day, swathed in pretty things.
In Jane's closet, you wear strong overalls.
No one will catch you, now that you can run.

The Women Wearing Hair Nets
stand behind the counter.
They make grilled cheese
and give you pudding for dessert.
The goldfish and turtles join you.
In the night they're set free and
give lectures on life before the tank.

Father God
lays out the robes for you to wear after dark.
Come, he says, try them on. Feed me the host.
He eats a bag of them, dipped in steak sauce,
chocolate milk, and your blood.
He opens the closet and his shiny black shoes dance
to his music. When the sun rises, the party's over,
he wipes your mouth and sends you home.

The Silver Sink
swallows you in its bigness.
In it you scrub pots during the day;
at night, it's your warm bubble bath.
The stains of the day disappear down the drain;
cleansed, you are safe in its moist darkness.

Night is a place, beyond time.
To enter you must have night vision.
The capacity to see what others don't.
Did you eat your carrots?

Healing Fantasy

If I had a daughter...

We would go on adventures every day—to the library and museum, to the mountains and sea. Wherever we go, she will be able to count on three meals a day. Before each meal we will reflect on the good way we are treating ourselves.

Interesting friends will surround her life. Children and adults of different colors, lifestyles, accents, and beliefs. She will learn that all are held equally by the graciousness of life.

She will never be left with a baby-sitter unless they are friends in whose company she feels safe and cared for. Her room will have lots of windows. She will always have a view of the world beyond her room. It will be her own room, and everyone must knock before entering.

She will be surrounded by images of women of all shapes and sizes so she will be proud of her body. Women's art, music, poetry, and books will fill our home. She will hear of men's accomplishments in the world—in our home, women's words and deeds will be heard and celebrated. We will read stories of women from around the world, women who are powerful and compassionate non-victims.

She will hear these words every day in the spirit of our interactions, in the quality of our silences, in the freedom of our adventures, in the eyes of our friends, in the healing darkness of our nights:

Run free like the wind. Jump high like a horse. Climb a tree. Cross a creek. Wrestle a friend to the ground. Tumble down a hill. Let your voice be heard by the whole world. Love your body. It is your teacher, healer, and challenge—your faithful companion for the length of your days. The exuberance of the universe pulsates through you. Be full of yourself!

Be sassy and loud. Question. Argue. Debate. Voice your truth. When you don't like your food, spit it out. When you're exhausted from tagging along in someone else's life, refuse to take another step. When you don't like someone and tighten in their presence, make your discomfort known. The truth of the universe pulsates through you. Be full of yourself!

Trust your vision of the world and express it. Love the sounds, movements, ideas, images, and words that bubble up from inside of you. Paint a picture, create a dance, make up a song, write a poem. Follow no script—you are a one-of-a-kind child of life. The originality of the universe pulsates through you. Be full of yourself!

Love your mind. Express your feelings. Use your time, energy, and attention in service of your own life. Remember yourself. Exist for yourself. Be desirable to yourself. Change your life if you want it changed. Do not wait for one to come. Your life begins anew each moment. The spirit of the universe pulsates through you. Be full of yourself!

Remember Your Wow-ness

Verse 1

Do you ever look up at the night sky and say WOW?
Well you're made of the same WOW-ness as the night sky.

Verse 2

Do you ever get lost in it's bigness and say WOW?
Well you're made of the same WOW-ness as the big sky.

Verse 3

Do you ever feel held by its darkness and say WOW?
Well you're made of the same WOW-ness as the dark sky.

Verse 4

Do you feel the tug of the full moon and say WOW?
Well you're made of the same WOW-ness as the full moon.

Verse 5

Do you ever try to count the stars and say WOW?
Well you're made of the same WOW-ness as the night stars.

Voice Choir

You are composed of the same stuff as the Milky Way.
You are an exquisite dimension of the Galaxy's development.
You are a space the Universe fashioned to feel its own grandeur.
You are an individualized expression of WOW. WOW!

Show and Tell

One Saturday night each month, Patty's friends and the friends of her parents are invited over for "Show and Tell." Patty's mother is usually the Queen of Ceremonies because she always wanted to be a comedienne but her parents wanted her to learn to type until she got married. She didn't listen to her parents, never learned to type, and is the official comedienne of the family, the neighborhood, and the PTA. She starts off with the same words and actions every month:

"Be full of yourself.
Brag, boast, and show-off.
Be pompous and big-headed.
Blow your own horn."
(She blows a horn and passes it around!)

"Be loud about what you can do.
Be too big for your britches.
Have your cake and eat it too."
(She cuts the cake and passes it around!)

"Everyone gets a standing ovation because it takes courage to show and tell in front of an audience. Sometimes it takes more courage for us grownups to sing and dance, to share our ideas, and to read our words, but we do it and we get a standing ovation too. Let's practice the ovation before we begin."
(Up and down until they've got it!)

One Saturday night, Patty was ready to sing her favorite country western song. She had been practicing all week even though she knew the words by heart since she was four years old. She was the first one introduced by her mother and stepped onto the stage as her sister started the tape. At just the right moment she began to sing (with Nancy Griffith's help) "Love at the Five and Dime." Patty invited everyone to join in at the chorus.

Patty got a standing ovation. At school they tell Patty that she doesn't have a voice. She knows this isn't true. She does have a voice and she hears herself use it every day. And Patty loves to sing. It makes her smile deep inside. So she doesn't listen to the people at school who tell her those things about her voice. She listens to her friends and family. She loves it when they say, "Wow, you're fantastic!" Or "That's a great song you taught us. I sang it all week." Or "Your face sparkles when you sing." Or "I'm so glad you are in my life!" Their words feel warm, like the sun calling her out to play on a summer day. Their words say what she knows is true. She is a special girl with a special voice, and she'll keep singing because it makes her smile!

The Divine Girl-Child

Chorus
Hold the baby. Tenderly love her.
Hold the baby. Tell her you care.

Verse 1
Welcome her joyfully. Shout with a loud voice:
"You belong here among us. We're glad you're alive!"

Verse 2
Look down upon her. Bless every movement.
She deserves loving kindness, every day of her life.

Verse 3
Surround her with goodness, safety, and laughter.
She is the Divine Child, come among us this day.

Verse 4
Look at her closely. There is no blemish.
She is a delight, soothing this world with peace.

Verse 5
Cherish the baby, living among us.
Care for her willingly, every day of her life.

Verse 6
Celebrate the girl-child, born in all ages.
Come to bring us salvation and grace.

Happenings

The Prom

Calvary Gospel Church frowned upon most of the activities that seemed like fun in high school, including dancing, dating, and kissing. A good Christian girl didn't do any of those things. In my sophomore year I walked away from God, which meant I refused to attend weekly youth group meetings and I began dating a senior named Sal DiBella. Sal was the most desirable Italian "hunk" at Arts High School. He was also a Catholic and, according to our church, not a Christian. Thus dating him was a serious offense.

Sal invited me to the senior prom. The senior prom was considered Satan's territory by the folks at church. Anything could happen there! Consequently, six months before the prom, I began spinning an elaborate lie to guarantee that my mom didn't find out about my grandest rebellion. I told her that end-of-year exams were going to be extremely difficult, and in preparation, I was starting a weekly study group with my friend Ellen at her apartment.

Our scheme went off without a hitch. The weekly study group provided the perfect cover for prom preparation. We spent the time dreaming up my outfit, scanning magazines for the perfect hairstyle, and counting pennies to purchase the necessary accoutrements. On the day of the prom, I went to Ellen's house. My gown was waiting for me. Ellen fixed my hair and makeup. I stepped into my gown.

Standing like a princess in the middle of the living room, waiting for my ride to the ball, I heard the door bell ring. Excitedly Ellen opened the door, expecting my prince to appear. Instead I watched in horror as my mother and the minister entered Ellen's living room. "God told me what you were up to. We came to rescue you," my mother said. "Oh my God," I exclaimed and ran into the bedroom. I changed my clothes and told Ellen that she *had* to wear my dress and go to the prom with Sal.

As my mother, the minister, and I were going down the steps from Ellen's second-floor apartment, Sal and his buddies were climbing the steps. We met halfway. "Where are you going?" Sal asked. Sobbing uncontrollably, I answered, "Ellen will explain."

It was silent in the van on the way home. My mother and the minister sat in front. I sobbed in the rear seat, my princess dreams broken at my feet. At about 11 P.M. the phone rang. It was Ellen. "Sal's coming to get you at 5 in the morning. Be ready for him. He has something to give you." At 5 A.M. I snuck out of our apartment and met Sal. He gave me a star sapphire surrounded by diamonds. We were going steady!

That summer, I was given no choice: I had to attend Bible camp. The pressure was unbearable there. Everyone was praying that rebellious Patty Reilly would return to God. They staged several all-night prayer meetings for me. Exhausted by the attention, I confessed my sins, the most horrific of which—even worse than attending the evil prom—was dating a non-Christian. Everyone rejoiced that day. I was told to write to Sal: *Dear Sal, I can't date you any more because you're not a Christian. I will pray for you. Good-bye. Patty*

That fall, late one evening, there was a knock on the door of our eleventh-floor apartment. "Who is it?" I asked through the door. "Sal and Bart," the stern response. "What do you want?" I murmured. "The ring."

Breaking up with an Italian hunk was risky business. Almost as risky as walking away from God. If I refused to give them the ring, I might have to contend with the Mafia. I ran into the bedroom, got the ring, disengaged the deadbolt, left the chains in place, and extended my trembling hand through the opening. They took the ring and left the hand intact, for which I was grateful!

Getting off the school bus one day that fall, Sal's younger brother Joey DiBella approached me:

"I read what you wrote in my brother's yearbook."

"What was that?" I asked.

"That you would love him forever. You didn't."

The Family Business

My father, the bookie, took me to the racetrack
during spring break from Princeton
on my first visit back to Los Angeles
since my mother packed us up
when I was five and hightailed out of town,
out of state, 3,000 miles across the country
to escape the harrowing challenges
of living with a violent alcoholic.

At some point my father put down the bottle
and chose gambling as his primary preoccupation.
How exactly the daughter of an alcoholic-turned-bookie
ended up at Princeton Seminary studying god
is another story for another time.
Suffice to say, my classmates were the children
of your run-of-the-mill middle-class professional folks:
clergy, lawyers, MDs, MBAs, and the like.
I was the *only* one in my class whose father was a bookie!
Bookie, short for *bookmaker*:
one who determines odds, receives and pays off bets.

So there we are, father and daughter, at Hollywood Racetrack, guide-
sheet in hand, my father teaching me about the art and science of
handicapping, describing the various measures and tools used to pick
a winner, outlining the history of horse racing, a sport dating back
4,000 years, peppering the technicalities with wisdom gleaned from
his bookie life:

"Winning and losing are seasonal."

"Addicts are in it for the quick win,
professionals are in it for the long haul."

"You've got to do your research:
know the facts, mix them with your intuition;
facts and gut work together to create a successful career."
My father, grooming me for the family business.

Why are you wasting your time at Princeton?, he asks.
You'd make lots more money following in my footsteps.
The streets are ready for a smart young woman like you!
"There's this thing about god I have to work out
before I can make any long-term decisions, Daddy."
Well how about a late night TV show about god—
those television evangelists make lots of money, he advised.
"I'm doing the research, Daddy. I'll keep you posted."

My next visit to LA was two years later in 1985. We were informed
of my father's death by his lawyer, a character right out of a seedy
detective novel, who got Daddy out of big trouble at some point.
"Your father owed me one," he said. "That's how I ended up executor
of his estate."

We found our way to Daddy's Inglewood apartment from the air-
port. It was sparsely furnished with rented furniture and no glimpses
of beauty. "Low-key was your father's MO so the cops wouldn't
become suspicious," the lawyer informed us. "You know, he was the
most successful bookie in LA county," he added on his way out the
door.

Now alone in the apartment, my sister and I sorted through my
father's possessions. I found a stack of letters on the mantel, tied with
a ribbon. He'd saved every letter I'd written him since age five. After
an hour of sorting, I discovered a stack of files and gasped as they
revealed just how successful a bookmaker my father had been.

For all those years my father, the bookie, had been assembling a
blue-chip stock portfolio for each of his daughters, nurtured from his
successful, albeit checkered, life as a gambler. Clearly he didn't trust the

income-producing capacities of my god-oriented vocational choices and decided early on to take my financial well-being into his own hands.

As a souvenir, I gathered the sheets of 8½ × 11 scrap paper my father would cut into tiny pieces on which to write the infamous numbers and bets that turned into our pot of gold. Upon returning to Princeton, I wrote the draft of my graduate thesis on his paper. A fitting reappropriation of the tools of Daddy's trade, the thesis led me to graduation, and eventually, to a self-supporting career as a book-maker in my own right.

Thank you, Daddy!

Dancing into Life

In 1986, I dreamt that I was being processed into a prison. I had to wait for an execution to secure a bed. Finally, I was issued one. A few days later, I was given a pass to go outside the prison for an appointment. No one accompanied me, yet I was reminded of my "prisoner" status by the crossing guards at each corner. I would be required to return. I arrived at a lovely house and asked the four sisters sitting in their kitchen, "Where is the Jewish dance teacher?" They scorned my disheveled appearance and reluctantly pointed out her room.

I don't remember what happened in her room. In the next scene, however, I was free and sitting outside of a beautiful yellow Victorian house with a group of women, including one of the four sisters I met earlier. It was our house! We were celebrating a performance we had just completed. Two of the "haughty" sisters approached our celebratory group. They thanked us for our dance performance, and then thanked me for helping their sister to heal through movement and dance. In gratitude, they handed me a check.

Several months after the dream, I attended a weeklong movement retreat. Each movement and sacred drama experience escorted me into the deep places of my being and invited the memories and emotions of childhood to be released. As the facilitator, Carla De Sola, and I moved together in a womb dance, I reexperienced the trauma of the turbulent nine months in my mother's womb, tossed to and fro by my parents' troubled relationship. I also reexperienced my deep ambivalence about entering the world. As we moved in synch, emotionally and in dance, my body groaned with the pain of a lifetime. With her support, I was able to push beyond my ambivalence and choose life. With the group's support as my labor coaches, the womb of the mother thrust me out of hiding toward visibility.

As Carla and I continued to experience a healing connection through movement, I was reminded of the dance teacher in the dream. I was puzzled because "De Sola" did not seem to be a Jewish name. When I asked her about it, she told me her family was indeed Jewish!

As a result of our sacred drama experience, my creativity began to unthaw. In the subsequent months, I danced, painted, and wrote the creativity of a lifetime. I decided to enroll in the Expressive Arts Therapy Program at Lesley College in Cambridge. Imagine my amazement as I arrived to register at the school and found myself standing outside an exact replica of the yellow Victorian in my dream. And in the seventeen years since the dream, I have received many checks in gratitude for my work as an Expressive Arts Facilitator, supporting women to heal through creativity.

Mama

I took my mother to the beach today.
Ashes to ashes and dust to dust.
In a container, carefully prepared in New Jersey,
where her life ended, complications due to Alzheimer's, they said.
In a container, carefully carried to California, where I began,
thrust from my young mother's womb, forty-two years ago.

I laughed with my mother at the beach today.
Ashes to ashes and dust to dust.
Wondered if I'd be sad.
Supposed to be sad, my mother's dead.
All that's left are her ashes, *cremains* they're called.
Laughter, however, was her final blessing.
Enough tears had been shed.

The wind danced with my mother at the beach today.
Ashes to ashes and dust to dust.
As I held out each handful of cremains to scatter them,
the wind picked my mother up
and danced playfully with her across the beach.
And then gently laid her down to final rest,
one handful at a time.

A little girl kissed my mother at the beach today.
Ashes to ashes and dust to dust.
A little girl picked up a shell.
"Is this your mother?" "Yes," I said.
She kissed the shell
and gave it to me: "Kiss her."
A kiss, my final blessing.

I kissed my mother at the beach today.
Ashes to ashes and dust to dust.

The Circle of Life

Week 4

I am pregnant for the first time in my life. I had unprotected intercourse with an ambivalent lover. Months of eating greens, saying *yes* to life, my life. Months of daily yoga, stimulating my feminine processes. What was I preparing for? My biological clock ticking, attracting a strong sexual partner. My biological clock, ordering my days and my nights.

I love children *and* I do not want a child. I have never used birth control. I have trusted my intuitive connection to my body. So one time I'm wrong. My womb wanted a child.

That was a juicy weekend. An inner franticness pursued me. I was moving toward men in an uncustomary way. Could it be that the womb takes one strong last gasp before it is no longer available to support life? Could it be that our romance had little to do with him? Was he chosen by my clock to be the one, the only one in forty-three years, whose sperm would meet an egg of mine and dance toward life?

Week 5

I spent a day with my sister. She needed my help choosing a wedding dress. I needed her help saying good-bye to the possibility of life. We acknowledged the child growing within me. We released its spirit: "Go now. At some future time may you be received by a joy-filled womb. A womb that will carry you full-term into life."

Rather than have my uterus vacuumed, I wanted to abort naturally. I wonder who invented the vacuum technique. I'd be surprised if it were a woman. I tried strong herbs and then went to the Ob-Gyn. She scheduled the surgical procedure with the option to cancel if I aborted naturally. They told me about an abortion study. I qualified for the two-part procedure.

Week 6

I was injected with Methatrexate, a chemical used in cancer treatment. In multiple doses it causes severe and long-lasting side effects. There would be no side effects with one dose, I was told. I felt nothing. Silently the chemical moved through me. Silently it arrested the growth of the fetus.

Week 7

One week later, on my way to a body-work training, I stopped by the clinic to receive vaginal suppositories to support the expulsion of the fetus. Would the fetus let go gently, with no more bleeding or cramping than a light period? Or would it fight for dear life as it passed through me?

As it turned out my body chose option two. It responded with bleeding and cramping unlike any period I have ever experienced. I chose to participate fully. I took no pills to ease the pain. To pass death/to let go of the possibility of life should hurt. I felt every cramp and breathed deeply until each one passed. I watched the river of blood flowing from me and touched the mother-fluid of life and death. I am woman. I am strong. Life gives me everything I need to participate in its ebb and flow.

While the other trainees were engaged in cathartic breathing, giving birth to themselves in sound and movement, I was in the hallway moving and stretching, moaning and groaning. Following every impulsive desire of my body without apology or shame. I crawled to the bathroom to vomit. I spread my legs far apart onto the wall and pressed until the cramping passed. I was giving birth and passing death at the same time.

Participants walked by me on their way to the bathroom. Some touched my head tenderly. A skillful midwife massaged my feet and coached my breathing. A gynecologist's daughter held my head. A strong man caught me as I was about to faint. A kind man silently supported me as I groaned the sorrow of many lifetimes.

After lunch on the second day of the training, a beautiful young woman danced with me. The six-week-old mass of potential was moving through me and we danced its passing. A mother's dance of sorrow for the passing of life into death. For the loss of a daughter, a possibility, a way of life. A No and Yes intertwined within me.

We die the way we have lived, they say. This is the way I'll die. I will participate in my own death. I will breathe my last breath with consciousness. Each day a practice in letting go. In allowing what is to be. In participating fully in the circle of life.

In wisdom, I acknowledge that everything changes. What is born will die. What dies nourishes life in its many forms. I honor both life and death. Neither do I elevate or despise. They are essential elements in the circle of life, in the circle of my life.

Reverie

After a hot and noisy afternoon of doing errands in the flatlands, I was grateful to board my bus and begin the luxurious climb home to the peaceful, shaded Berkeley hills. The road into the hills breaks free of the boring predictability of streets and corners. Like a woman's body it slopes and curves, seducing me to relinquish "To Do" lists and research challenges. The quiet descends, draining my body of the city's noisiness. The clean air invites me to breathe—finally a deep breath after a morning of careful breathing. Views of the bay and beyond open to me, and my heart expands in the comforting spaciousness.

Awakened from my sensual reverie by the exit of five talkative UC Berkeley students, I was now alone with the bus driver. "How do you like this route?" I asked her. "Too quiet. It's eerie up here. Don't know what's hiding in the quiet. I can only take this route for a while longer then I'm going to ask my supervisor for my old route back."

"Where's your old route?" I asked. "Oakland, downtown. The cars, the people, the noise. It's alive there. Up here, there's dead quiet. That's just it—dead, nothing's alive and no music either. My kids would be lonely up here. You never see kids playing in the street or neighbors talking. And the driving's harder. None of these streets are straight. They all curve like the curls on my grandbaby's head. They get me dizzy. In my neighborhood the streets are straight. You know where you're going and where you come from. Up here they circle around. On my first run I kept circling and circling, felt like a cat chasing its tail. Makes no sense at all."

"What about the views, you must enjoy them?" I asked, grasping for one common thread in our world view. "If I want a view I go to Jack London Square. We don't live far from there and I can touch and smell the water of the bay. I like to feel its coolness on my hands after driving all day. All you folks do is look. If I want to look, I'll buy a postcard. Rather be in the water or driving across the bridge. My kids and I like doing that."

"I get off here. Thanks!" I said interrupting her reverie. She finished, "Different strokes for different folks—that's what my Nana used to say. Good talking to you."

Breasts

To know anything at all
about our history, our bodies, ourselves,
we must reach beyond
what they told us,
what they taught us,
what they want from us,
we must reach back
to the very beginning.

Before merriam and webster,
who have something to say about everything:
"breast, a noun, either of two milk-producing glandular organs
on the front of the chest especially in the human female."

Before the reversals of christian history:
adam giving birth to the woman,
father god suckling the child,
christ nursing humanity,
the milk-giving goddess agatha claimed as their saint,
her breasts cut off and carried on a platter.

Before the alterations of the hebrew bible:
el shaddai, a name for god,
shaddai meaning breast,
male translators altered the meaning,
their "god of the high places" doesn't have breasts like mine.

We must reach back to the very beginning
to the place where lovers go
when they suck my breasts
to the source of life/mama mama mama
cried in the silence as their wet lips

surround my nipple
and they suck for dear life.

In the very beginning
long before adam gave birth
and father god sprouted breasts
and christ nursed humanity
and *shaddai* meant "high places"
and agatha's breasts were amputated
and my lovers wanted more than I could give
in the very beginning
was the big mama.

From her moon-breasts
flowed the milky way,
the stars and planets,
streams, rivers, and oceans,
all that ebbs and flows,
all that expands and contracts,
returning always to mama's breast.

To her breasts
pharaohs and kings
returned again and again
hoping to receive immortality
to become infants forever
nursing at mama's breast.

She came to me early in the morning
the one with breasts like mine
she held me in her arms
as i cried mama mama mama
don't let them take my breast away on a platter
her nipple found my lips
and i sucked for my dear life.

The breast-less surgeon,
the one they call artist
he cut into my breast
with skill and beauty
and all they took away that day
was a perfectly shaped lump
they left the breast.

She came to me again that night
the one with breasts like mine.
she brought agatha.
agatha brought her platter.
we made an altar in the middle of the forest.
on agatha's platter we placed her breasts and my lump.
using merriam and webster,
the hebrew scriptures, the christian bible,
and photos of lovers who became infants at our breasts,
as kindling, we built a fire and toasted marshmallows.

*Where two or three women are gathered together
there she is in the midst of them.*

A Service of Memory

To honor Ana Marley's life
and to acknowledge her death.

Sunday, August 25, 1996 ·:· 2:30 PM
Circle of Life Women's Center
1606 Bonita Avenue ·:· Berkeley, California 94707

Ana Marley
April 28, 1950–August 22, 1996

·:· ·:· ·:·

Prelude   *The Sounds of Nature*

A Call to Gather   *Patricia Lynn Reilly*
Ana Marley, Born April 28, 1950. Died August 22, 1996.
Daughter of Frank and Anna.
Sister of John, Tom, Mary, and Frank.
Mother of Erin and Robin.
Compassionate Friend.
Woman of Goodness, Creativity, and Grace.

We have come here today to honor the incredible life and to
acknowledge the death of Ana Marley. In wisdom, we acknowledge that everything changes. What is born will die. What dies
nourishes life in its many forms. We honor both life and death.
Neither is elevated nor despised. They are essential elements in the
circle of life.

An Invocation of Spirit   *Patricia Lynn Reilly*
Spirit of Life called by many names: Goddess, God, Christ, Buddha,
Mother, Father, Intuition, Deeper Wisdom, Truest Self, Source,
Creative Flow, Mystery. Be here among us.

Spirit of the Natural World: Place of comfort and inspiration for Ana, from the beaches of Greece to the vineyards of France; from the lakes of Tahoe to the island waters of the Bahamas, from the hot springs to the hiking trails of northern California. Be here among us.

Spirit of the Breath: Holding within you the essence of Ana and of all our ancestors. Be here among us.

Spirit of the Silence: Holding within you all memory and emotion, all things said and unsaid, all moments shared and unshared. Be here among us.

Readings	*Robin Marley*
Musical Offering	*Kate Wolf*
A Gathering of Memories	*Family and Friends*
Healing Through Creativity	*Ana's Words*

I was diagnosed with malignant melanoma in July 1993. The diagnosis left me feeling a full range of emotions. Rather than choosing to "battle" the disease; I choose to "dance" with it. In doing so, I have incorporated a personalized healing regime involving massage, hypnotherapy, acupuncture, and the Expressive Arts.

Many of us learned from a teacher, parent, or other well-meaning adult that we didn't have the talent to draw, paint, write, dance, or sing. We gave up on our creative selves. My classes provide a safe environment, enabling women and men to support one another to recapture the childhood joys of creativity. Using a variety of media, we will step onto the creative path. Guided imagery will connect us with our creative centers. Journal writing will allow us to dialogue with our own creative processes.

Musical Offering	*Chris Williamson*

A Blessing   *Patricia Lynn Reilly*

As we grieve the absence of Ana's physical presence among us, let us honor the spirit of Ana within us. Each time we take a deep breath in celebration of life flowing in, through, and around us; each time we choose to be present in this moment; each time we set free the images, sounds, movements, and words that clamor within us; each time we dance with "what is" rather than battling it; we honor Ana's spirit.

Go in peace, Ana. We grieve the absence of your physical presence among us. We honor your spirit breathing through our hearts and memories.

Go in peace, Ana's family and friends. Grieve the absence of her physical presence among us. Honor her spirit dancing through your hearts and memories.

Hot Flash

My trusty 1986 Toyota Celica died in a blaze of glory on April 24, 2000.
It all began with a hot flash, those pesky "episodes" accompanying the
retirement of one's reproductive organs, on my way to Montclair for
lunch. To cool off, I turned on the fan and within a few blocks, smoke
filled the car, billowing from the dashboard vents. I turned left onto
the first available street, grabbed my keys and bag, and jumped out of
my smoking car. The street turned out to be the entry driveway to the
Piedmont Utility Yard. The guys at the yard attempted to quiet the
smoke with fire extinguishers, to no avail. The smoke turned into
flames. Piedmont's fire department arrived within five minutes. One-
quarter of a tank of water later, the fire extinguished, all that was left
of my car was its steel skeleton.

Gone were my stuffed animals sitting in the vacant holes where
stereo speakers once resided, speakers stolen in the Berkeley Hills.
Gone were the plastic flowers given to me by a beloved friend of my
mother's while they were in a New Jersey nursing home together. Gone
were the contents of the glove compartment, an accumulation of years:
maps, expired car registrations and insurance cards, directions jotted
on scraps of paper. Gone was my longest term companion. Bought
new in 1986, my Celica and I traveled 130,000 miles together—
meaningful, non-commuter, alternate route, open road miles.

I am grateful for the good road life we shared and for my Toyota's
graceful end. Imagine if the fire had occurred on a main thorough-
fare—streets blocked, traffic jammed, folks angry, smoke and fire
endangering pedestrians, drivers, businesses, and homes. Instead its
dramatic end happened on a rarely traveled street, in a non-residen-
tial area, adjacent to the public works yard, with a bevy of emergency-
oriented men at my disposal! AAA took my car to a "dismantler" in
Berkeley. A friend picked me up at the Utility Yard and delivered me
home, safe and sound, just in time to walk to a friend's memorial service, my first official outing as an urban hiker.

In the Basement

Throughout my stay in Ireland I heard rumors about Sheila na Gig, Ireland's one remaining life-and-death goddess. Her name means "sheila of the breasts." She is a brazen goddess who grins from a squatting position while holding her vagina open with both hands. One afternoon I stopped in a reggae record shop, needing to make contact with non-caucasians even if that contact was limited to posters on the walls and voices from the speakers—Ireland is monotonously homogeneous. The owner chatted about his dream-come-true of owning a record shop. His friend Jeff arrived and we shifted topics to feminist theology. Jeff, a pagan, had studied pre-Christian Ireland. The Sheila na Gig image was carved into stone doorways, he said, offering protection and blessing to those who passed under her. Not easily eliminated in the transition from goddess to god, the Catholic Church found it necessary to incorporate her sculptures as gargoyles in its churches. Women, on their way out of Mass, reached up and touched the stone sculpture's open vulva and proud belly as their fertility prayer.

In the 1950s the Catholic powers-that-be, embarrassed by Sheila na Gig's genital-displaying tendencies, scoured the country for her remaining sculptures, confiscated them from their ancient resting places, and whisked them away to the basement of the National Museum in Dublin. As I listened to Sheila na Gig's story, my new life mission crystallized: I would liberate Sheila from the basement! A few days later, I walked into a specialty shop in Ennis to browse and told the clerk about my mission. She offered to mobilize Irish women for the adventure. We imagined wearing costumes and presenting performance pieces outside the Museum to draw attention to Sheila's imprisonment, *and* to divert attention from our team of crack goddess-rescuers making their way to the basement. "And by the way," she said matter-of-factly, "one of the few intact Sheila na Gig sculptures is ten miles outside town on the portal of a 1,000-year-old church." She drew a map and I was on my way!

Because I chose to bus-it through Ireland, it was necessary for me to hire an accomplice. I was directed to a cab company and asked its one woman driver, "Will you take me on an adventure?" Intrigued, and grateful for the work, Carmel said yes and we were off. She drove us to the church and a university student on a similar quest led us to the squatting goddess, full of herself and her vulva. "Wow," I said as I touched the goddess. I stood in front of this powerful image with ancient flesh and open vagina, grateful for her tenacious presence in Ireland, requesting her support to love my changing body. Observing my antics from a distance, Carmel was planning what she'd tell her family and friends about this once-in-a-lifetime escapade: "a crazy woman from California kidnapped me and took me to the goddess, that's what I'll tell them!"

Our next mission was to find the local author, PJ Morgan, who wrote a short story about Sheila na Gig and lived within a few country blocks of the church. We drove down a narrow road and found his home. He graciously answered my questions. He told us that after consigning the stone carvings to the basement, the museum staff put "nippies" on the Sheila na Gig stones. "What are nippies?" I asked. He and Carmel laughed. "Diapers," they said in unison. Embarrassed by her exposed vagina, the powers-that-be put diapers on the sculptures. Most secular Irish folks, PJ added, were actually mortified to imagine world-renown archaeologists and anthropologists arriving in Dublin to view these rare and treasured pre-Christian relics, being escorted to the basement to discover diapered Sheila na Gigs.

Back at home now, plans for the rescue have been postponed. I see Sheila often though, in my mind's eye, and remember those silent moments standing in front of her powerful image. She grins at me—her ancient flesh, her yawning vagina, her boldness and freedom insisting that I emerge from the basement; that I refuse to cover the beauty of my changing body; and that, in this season, I embrace it all, regardless!

Tribute to the Unitarians

My father, the bookie, is applauding in his grave.
More precisely, his cremains are shivering with delight
in their various resting places: at hollywood racetrack,
a fitting choice given the time he spent there,
(and our one non-judgmental bow to his livelihood),
and on a beach in Malibu, a not-so-fitting choice,
fulfilling our wish for an elegant ending to his unorthodox life.

My father, whose final days were spent
taking bets from his hospital bed
after his third or fourth bypass surgery,
finally has reason to be proud of his eldest,
who wasted her time in theological school
and refused his vocational advice:
"If you're going to be a minister,
at least be a TV preacher, they make lots of money."

Finally proud, because I now belong to a church
filled with other children of gamblers
who play poker late into the night at church retreats.
After circling their table for an hour or so,
I surrendered to the "familiar energy,"
and played poker for the first time,
invoking my father's spirit for inspiration.
Beginner's luck, genetic inheritance, or a prayer answered,
whatever, I won piles of nickels at the table that night.

The Clearing

a clearing beckons me.
it is in the distance,
yet my arrival there is certain.

it is a wide open space
deep within the forest of my being.
its floor layered with seasons passed,
its canopy woven from time's evolving.
a place of deep rest, of sparkling clarity,
of strong purpose, of tender heart's desire.
green and growing, fertile and sacred.

on the way there,
out of the confusion, the burden, the longing,
out of all that's been and will never be again,
a path opens, a spiral path,
inviting me to follow it round and round again
toward the spaciousness at the center of all that is.

escorts appear—skillful teachers and healers, lovers and friends,
offering me a word, a touch, a truth,
reminding me of the way when I get lost,
of the certainty of my arrival when I despair.
the spirit of life, the faithful rhythm of the breath
pulsates in and through and around me,
echoing ancient wisdom to accompany me along the way:

Elevate not the beginning. Despise not the ending.
All is seasonal, not harsh.
Honor coming and going, holding on and letting go,
joy and sorrow, reunion and separation.

Hold onto nothing. Participate in everything.
Notice all that is and bless it, as it shifts and changes in a moment.
A full emptiness, unfolding from the center—
always new, always now, always and not yet, always and never.

a clearing beckons me.
it is in the distance
yet my arrival there is certain.

Encounters

Culinary Quiz

this inquiring mind wants to know
what do I taste like?

lima beans?
a nectarine?
california sushi?
swiss chard?
white beans?
bailey's irish creme?
fish and chips?
a strawberry?

am i sweet, sour, bitter, salty?
am i dry or juicy? creamy, or clear like a broth?
am i a snack, an appetizer, a main course, or dessert?

does my heart taste like my mind?
do my words taste like my presence?

so tell me, what do I taste like?
i've always wondered.

Spring Juices

spring juices flowing
the fragrance of attraction
rousing me from winter's celibate sleep
awakening the erotic in every encounter
with bus driver, musician, old friend.

moistened by a contagious ecstasy,
i open and receive the fertile darkness,
a friend's laugh, the calla lily's curves,
the yam's sweetness, an old woman's fierceness,
the egret's pose, the musician's sounds,
the call of my ancestors, the fleshiness of *all* that is.

i wonder what it would be like
for us to be lovers in the moist spring.
to dance with each other's ideas
on a blanket at the park, perhaps;
stroking, teasing, tasting, opening,
expanding the ideas until they formed
a beautiful poem, an ode to "what is."

our bodies aroused, moistened, and opened
by the dance of our minds,
by the play of our words;
our bodies attune to the hum,
the resonance, the *ah*,
our bodies erupting on a shared bed
in response to the dance, to life, to *It*.

Accoutrements of Passion

last night i filled an armoire
with sensual accessories: fragrances to seduce,
textures to tantalize, colors to delight;
and with the accoutrements of passion:
handcuffs, a whip, ties, and ropes;
candles and toys; leather and silk;
wigs, gloves, clothes, and shoes
for every mood, for every character within me:
the temptress, the victim, the masochist,
the fighter, the dancer, the whore, the saint.

a work in progress to be filled as my fetishes emerge,
to fit my ever-changing moods for pain and pleasure,
for sternness and play, for severity and gentleness,
for freedom and bondage, for spirit and flesh.

isn't it true that we are *both* spirit and flesh,
that our impulses toward *ah* and *om*
rise from our ancestral origins?
i wonder: will they applaud at sunday's service
if i testify of my discoveries;
if i dance in honor of *all* i find within me?

Words Made Flesh

gathering the glimpses
lingering to touch, taste, and wonder

respect
re-spectare
to look again

from abstraction to fleshiness
from platforms and positions to vulnerability
from words to sentences to paragraphs to systems

our little systems have their day
they have their day and cease to be
broken lights   fingers pointing

fleshy words/words made flesh
    sleeping ducks
    solitary night herons
    seaweed, sushi, and salmon
    lust for life in all its fluidity
    dare with me
    bite into life
    and the fullness
    of its possibility
    a kiss on the cheek

painful ruptures
bones of anguish
fear of boundedness
erotic invasions
suffocation

a descent
room to breathe

silence to receive
spaces between
and around
and within things
radiance   wholiness
the maternal deep

beyond longing
beyond imagination
beyond words
to incarnation
to connection
to healing in the flesh
erotic openings   bliss

resurrection
reconstitution
love worthiness
redemptive re-enactment

fleshy words/words made flesh
    the embrace
       opening   receiving
       more than touch
       less than grasping
       a beholding
       to be held
       we are made
       for the embrace

where are you
i am close by
warm heart
smiling eyes

Confession

it follows me everywhere
even into love
no relief, no place to rest
destined to wander
from solitude to hunger
and back again.

ordinary men
unable to match the growling hunger
the dancing wildness,
the unquenchable desire to moisten,
to open, to let them in
their guilt or fear or memories
rise up to quench the beast.

they refuse to go to the edges
where i must go
when the warm turns to hot within me
no cool down since he visited me in the night
since they downed me in the field
since his lens captured my panting
my adolescent moistness
turning into a flood of desire
before his eyes.

arousal my demanding lover,
teases my nipples
swells my vulva
awakens the growl
it threatens to tell on me
to release the flood
to extract the sounds

to demand a dance
even in public places.

god quieted it for me
my freshman year in high school
an answered prayer
i couldn't announce at church meetings
and then it happened again
the fire rising from some untouchable depth
uncoiling to meet him
when mommy left for night work
and i let him in.

god took charge after that
and everything was quiet
until I fired him at thirty
a vow, my most recent restraint
while I vomited
the two-year binge with strangers
together we went to the edges
where growling turns into screams
and no one listens
and everyone is baby or god
and the back of someone
is your kiss good-night.

quieted until you asked to kiss my cheek
in front of whatever god
watches over unitarians
it awakened again
right there in fellowship hall
in front of everyone
it threatened to tell on me.

Sacred Kisses

My First Kiss

I remember preparing for my first kiss. I don't remember if the kiss actually happened. Kenny DeBaun was the star of our elementary school basketball team. He dedicated each successful basket to me. I was flattered. My girlfriends insisted on teaching me how to kiss. We rendezvoused in the choir loft above the chapel a few times a week. The girls showed me how to position my lips for the inevitable kiss and how to ready my body for his embrace.

We practiced in the dark choir loft to avoid detection by our teachers, the Sisters of St. Joseph, but we knew God saw everything. He was everywhere, they said, even in your mind, heart, and body. He could see your every thought and feeling, wish and dream. He knew your every move. I felt scared, and rebellious, knowing God was watching as I practiced puckering my lips and readying my body for the forbidden embrace.

A Kiss on Holy Hill

Decades later I sat peacefully at a booth in the back corner of a Berkeley restaurant, reviewing the schedule for a Dance and Religion conference I was in town to attend. My dinner arrived. The fish was cold. I turned to call the waitress and there he was, sitting at the booth behind mine. Our eyes met. He introduced himself and joined me at my booth. We shared a salad, my warmed-up fish arrived, we spoke of love and life and books, and then Michael and I ventured out of the restaurant to dance at two local clubs.

At the end of the evening, long past midnight, Michael dropped me off at the corner where LeConte, Ridge, and Scenic meet, the conference location: Pacific School of Religion. "Oh you're staying on holy hill," he informed me. "Holy hill," I puzzled aloud. "The hill where the gods live," he clarified. We exchanged addresses and phone numbers in case I visited California again or he found himself in

Massachusetts. And then a kiss, a juicy mouth-to-mouth, filled with hope-of-the-future, kiss on god's holy hill. "Keep in touch," he said as we parted.

Which gods were watching that evening, I wondered as I strolled to my dorm. Was it god the father, the god of my early years? From what I remembered of him, he would have been displeased by such a kiss on his holy hill, impure thoughts and all that. Or was it mother god? I'm sure she would have been upset with me as well for kissing a stranger. What of the goddess? Had she arrived on holy hill? Did such things disturb her? Or would she have smiled if she were watching that evening?

What gods reside in sacred places these days? Are they kiss-friendly? Do any of their religions celebrate the erotic, the pleasurable, the passionate? To find out, I will travel around the world with my lover, kissing in sacred places.

Daddy-Shaped Lovers

Our first serious conversation was at the card catalog in the graduate school library. From the moment we met, I knew my heart had attached to David in a familiar manner, both exhilarating and frightening. I wrote in my journal that evening: "My heart, persistent in its ways, has been drawn again to a man with Daddy's energy—a familiar energy. Will this man of passion leave as Daddy did? Will I ever experience passion's permanence with such a one?"

Although aware of the pattern and its potential danger, my heart persisted. David, the lost one who must be found; David, whose brilliance must be uncovered and fanned to life. Soon we were eating every meal together and studying together at the library, usually at my initiative. Tantalized by occasional moments of beauty, my every thought revolved around him. I was caught in the swirl of his pain, his choices, and his dreams. My life was completely absorbed by his.

It's the moments of beauty I'm drawn toward: moments of beauty followed by an all too familiar withdrawal. The little girl is seduced by a familiar energy—her daddy gives her silver dollars and chocolate milk, then he withdraws, he goes away for weeks at a time. The little girl always hopes it will be different, always hoping her daddy will stay, hoping David will turn toward her, for longer than a moment.

David never did offer more than moments. Eventually he wandered away toward another distraction without saying good-bye, just as Daddy had done many years before. Please come back, Daddy. I'll be good.

A familiar energy, a familiar script, a familiar ending. I long for an original relationship—face to face, for longer than a moment.

A Lover's Question

"Will you yield to the openings of heart?"

My heart is tender, tentative, most familiar with solitary adventures, occasionally risking significant connection, unsure and unsteady for lack of practice, for fear of breaking.

To yield is to let go of an old story...that love triggers pain. To yield is to write a new story, to imagine heart-healing in the company of a lover. To yield is to rest in the arms of *Life* holding my sweet, tender, tentative, solitary heart. To bless it with a kiss.

The kiss reminds me of how brave I have been to open my heart to *Life*. Love has been more challenging, but my heart receives every blessing, challenge, and experience *Life* brings to me. I smile in this moment realizing that *Life* has been my lover, my friend since childhood. And I am grateful.

Thank you for your question.

A Matching Yes

On this day I ask for an indication of your certainty—not about outcomes, but an indication of your desire, your availability, and your "fitness" to journey with me. The journey requires a matching yes to the simple heart-gestures of attraction, availability, and spaciousness. I've learned that mismatched adventures are depleting.

I am interested enough to turn toward you regularly, to touch, taste, and sense, inspired by gratitude for the dance of our words made flesh. *Are you interested enough to sustain attention across the distance?*

I am available. I have made no promises. I am free to follow the star wherever it may lead. *Are you truly available to follow the star of this rising or is your heart promised to another, your intimacy-energy more appropriately turned toward her?*

I have room to bite into our encounters and the fullness of their possibility. My life is spacious, always expanding to hold attractions of mind, heart, and body. *Is there room in this season of your life to play with me in the deep places?*

I will await your response before I continue to offer you the beauty of my open heart and the depth of my attention.

Imagine Lovers

Imagine lovers...

Who smile in each other's company.
They say a strong and sensual YES to each other.
Their YESes meet and fill their experience.

Who tell the truth about what works and what doesn't.
They co-create solutions for their shared challenges.
No truth is too hard for them to speak or hear.

Who spend purposeful time together.
They cultivate life-affirming friends and experiences.
They share the everyday details of life with ease and grace.

Who guard each other's solitude.
They cultivate spaces in their togetherness.
They delight in each other's individuality.

Who turn toward each other with heart-full attention.
Their sexual and orgasmic impulses are moistened by their
emotional connection and flow naturally in each other's presence.

Who support each other's creative impulses and expression.
They welcome and encourage shared creative adventures.
They aren't afraid to color outside the lines.

Who share a spiritual practice of silence and reflection
to stay in alignment with the essence of their love.
Gratitude for ALL THAT IS fills their relationship.

And so it is!

Happiness to Thy Sheets

I'm hot—no more flannel sheets.
Your feet are too cold—wear socks.
If you must fart—please leave the bed.
You're always so far away—come closer.
My feet are cramped—untuck the covers.
You're hogging the covers—give me some.
Eat in the kitchen—no crumbs in my bed.
You're taking up all the space—move over.
These are the tensions.

Hot versus cold.
Light versus dark.
Chaos versus control.
Covers versus no covers.
Process versus destination.
Freedom versus confinement.
Spooning versus separateness.
Diagonal versus parallel positioning.
These are the issues.

To eat or not to eat...in bed.
To wear or not to wear...pajamas.
To use or not to use...flannel sheets.
To tuck or not to tuck...in the sheets.
To measure or not to measure...with a ruler.
To allow or not to allow...the cat, dog, and canary in the bed.
These are the questions.

Reflections

Razor's Edge

It's exhausting bumping up against the same edge over and over again, a habit of thought and response, ancient and familiar. I've been aware of this particular edge since childhood. I wrote about it in adolescent journals as my "thorn in the flesh." I believe that our deepest impulse is toward health and wholeness, and with this belief I support others to choose health over and over again. Yet my "habit" seems so tenacious. Sometimes I despair of being free of it.

I was encouraged in adolescence by Paul's acknowledgment of his unnamed "thorn" in the flesh and his need to accept it as impenetrable. Are there impenetrable patterns? This one has accompanied me for so long, existing alongside my boundless health, vitality, and creativity. It demands of me a commitment to sustained consciousness, vigilance, and meditation. Sometimes this demand feels like a blessing—the radiance at the center of even our most frustrating limits. Sometimes this demand feels like a curse—an excruciating razor's edge, impossible to sustain.

Is it true, as someone once wrote, that *yes* is the original word and that no breach of this word will finally triumph? In the fullness of time will the *yeses* I have spoken swallow the trembling *no*? Will the choices for healing embrace, finally and completely, this injured vulnerability? Or must I embrace it, over and over again, as teacher, healer, and challenge, obeying its demands to surrender.

Do you ever despair of being free of historic vulnerabilities, free of habits of thought and behavior? Do yes and no clamor within you?

A Holy Task

Reason,
Your task is holy, yet you rebel.
You desire to be god.
To frame reality.
To reduce meaning.
To encompass being within your constructs.

Submit to your task.
Prepare the way for the holy.
Reveal to us our incomprehensibility,
the riddle of our natures.
Push us to the Paradox,
the unknown beyond explanation.
Then step aside.

Fear not that which you don't understand.
Allow the Paradox to bestow itself.
Embrace it, for in its arms we are transformed.

Waiting

Waiting is a way of life.
Monumental or mundane,
it's woven into the reality of our existence.

I waited with a friend while her son was undergoing surgery:
watching the clock, flipping the pages of a magazine,
jumping at each opening door—
perhaps this stretcher holds her son.
Moments held together by the thread of hope,
the child will be safe and well.
A delay sent a shiver through our hope.

I have waited for a boring class to end:
doodling on the mimeographed handout,
watching the minute hand as it journeyed toward dismissal time,
gathering my books slowly and quietly.
Moments held together by the thread of hope,
the time after class would be more fun!

A friend and I waited,
concert tickets in one hand, umbrella in the other
under the eaves of stadium bleachers: watching the sky,
pleading with the rain to go away and come again another day,
commiserating with fellow concert-goers.
Moments held together by the thread of hope,
we would soon see and hear Michael Jackson live in concert.

I have waited for one to return my love:
listening for the phone to ring,
looking for that tell-tale sparkle in his eyes,
longing for a kiss to transform us into lovers.
Moments and days held together by the thread of hope,
friends in love, maybe today will be the day!

Monumental and mundane,
the operation was a success;
the boring class ended and after class held better times;
the Jackson concert was postponed;
my love was never returned.

The early Christian church was waiting. Christ said he was going to return. The angels at his ascension assured his followers that he would come again as he had been taken. The church stood on tiptoe with expectation. They formed communities, rich and poor alike, sharing a common hope, waiting together for his arrival. They withstood the pressures of a hostile society, knowing that their Lord would return soon. To be ready, they lived simply as he had lived. Their hope was certain!

His return was delayed, however, and this led to deepening doubt and uncertainty in the early church. According to Jesus' parables, some took advantage of the delay to be irresponsible, as did the foolish servant. Others fell asleep, as the maidens did while waiting for the bridegroom, oil-less they were unable to endure the waiting period. The fearful ones dug holes in the ground to hide their talents, not sure how to live while waiting. As the years passed the church attached to more tangible hopes. Society kept its promises, at least some of them.

Centuries have passed. Is the church still waiting? Waiting for the pledge cards to arrive at the church office, for new drapes in the lounge, for the problem family to leave the fold. Waiting for what everyone else is waiting for…a bigger and better church building, a van for the youth, a call from a more prestigious parish. Mirroring the society around us, we accumulate and become attached to the upwardly mobile hopes of society. No longer expectant, we have settled down, claiming our piece of the pie.

We reflect society's distinctions as well. No longer sharing a common hope, we have churches for the rich and churches for the poor. We create special programs and missions for anyone unlike us. Distance is maintained through a specially trained staff to minister to the needs of the "marginal."

The church no longer needs to wait.
We are no longer poor.
We no longer suffer.

Lance Morrow aptly described the class distinctions of waiting
in a Time magazine essay, "Waiting as a Way of Life":

One of the most depressing things about being poor in America is the end-less waiting it entails: waiting for medical care at clinics or in emergency rooms, waiting in welfare or unemployment lines. The waiting rooms of the poor are forlorn. But one of the inestimable advantages of wealth is the immunity it can purchase from serious waiting. The rich do not wait—help sees to it. The limousine takes the privileged right out onto the runway, their shoes barely graze the ground.

We are comfortable now
and immune from serious waiting.
Our shoes barely graze the ground.

Pillows of Support

The week after I began writing my first book, I sat at the computer unable to work. Rather than berate myself, I listened to the resistant part of me. An anxious voice emerged. Through a written dialogue with "The Anxious One," it became clear that the level of focus and attention required of the writing project was overwhelming me. I asked "The Anxious One" how I might support her. I began setting up "pillows of support" around my life in order to go the distance with the creative project.

My first commitment was to weekly body work. I wrote a check for the first month's sessions to assure the anxious part of me that I was serious about attending to my body's needs. Each day I checked in with the Anxious One, "Now may I go back to work?" No, was the clear response. The second pillow of support was weekly attendance at a writers' group. We offered each other ongoing encouragement and feedback. I checked in again— still not enough support.

My third pillow was two full days off every week as a reminder that my life was more than the writing project. As I assembled this rich assortment of pillows, the anxious part of me relaxed. Three weeks later, having listened to the deep wisdom of my own life, met its needs with tenderness and grace, and designed my days in accordance with its feedback, I returned to my writing tasks without effort.

When we *panic* in response to the challenges of life, we are prone to second-guess our impulses, to pathologize our decisions, to theorize about our feelings, and to endlessly process and complain about our lives and relationships. Based on our earliest socialization, we long for a savior to come along and fix the situation for us. When this dependency-based response to life and its challenges becomes habitual, our creative resources lay dormant within us.

On the other hand, when we *participate* in the challenges of life, we take responsibility for our decisions, feel our feelings, actively engage our lives and relationships, and celebrate our own stunning capacities as children of life. Our creative capacities rise to meet the challenge and we take action on our own behalf with clarity and strength.

Based on the distinction between panic and participation, I encourage women to compose a vow of faithfulness to themselves. The vow process has been especially helpful to women during transitional moments when they are in that in-between life-space—neither here nor there—stepping into the unknown as they begin a new life-situation or leave a career, relationship, way of life, or self-understanding. Some transitions have a hard edge—they are thrust upon us without our consent. It's easy to panic when all the "neatness," predictability, and security of our lives, relationships, or health have shattered into a hundred pieces, laying in a chaotic mess at our feet due to an unexpected diagnosis or the sudden loss of a job or loved one.

Other transitions are chosen: folks choose to leave good jobs for even better ones, to bring closure to effective therapeutic relationships, or to move beyond no-longer-working friendships or partnerships. Still other transitions, like graduation from high school, college, or graduate school, are part of the benevolent flow of life. When we're moving from one situation to another due to circumstance or choice, we can lose our balance.

No matter the type of transition, the vow composition process provides the grounding necessary to create safe passage through transitional seasons of life. Refusing to entertain the question "who will save me," the process supports us to create strategies to address life-challenges by tapping into our own resources of creativity and wisdom and by gathering pillows of support to accompany us through challenging times. Incorporating the lessons of the past and the possibilities of the future, while firmly grounded in the present moment, the vow becomes our north star, our guiding light, the faithful breath we return to in the midst of the "creative chaos" of transition. The vow supports us to embrace our own life, valuing its lessons above the prescriptions of experts, and to participate fully in the challenges of life, using them as an opportunity to sharpen our skills for conscious living.

A Free Imagination

In the very beginning of her life, the girl-child has direct access to the spirit of life. It is as near to her as the breath that fills her. And it connects her to everything. She is not alone. Her spirit is one with the spirit of her beloved grandmother, of her favorite rock, tree, and star. She develops her own methods for contacting the spirit in all things.

She climbs a tree and sits in its branches, listening. She loves the woods and listens there too. She has a special friend—a rock. She gives it a name and eats her lunch with it whenever she can. She keeps the window open next to her bed even on the coldest of nights. She loves the fresh air on her face. She pulls the covers tight around her chin and listens to the mysterious night sky. She believes that her grandmother is present even though everyone else says she is dead. Each night, she drapes the curtain over her shoulders for privacy, looks out the window near her bed, listens for Grandma and then says silent prayers to her.

Her imagination is free for a time. She needs no priest or teacher to describe God to her. Spirit erupts spontaneously in colorful and unique expressions. God is Grandma, the twinkling evening star, the gentle breeze that washes across her face, the peaceful quiet darkness after everyone has fallen asleep, and all the colors of the rainbow. And because she is a girl, her experience and expression of spirit is uniquely feminine. It flows from her essence as naturally as the breath. The spirit of the universe pulsates through her. She is full of herself.

Eventually the girl-child will turn away from the Spirit-Filled One. Her original spirituality will become confined within the acceptable lines of religion. She will be taught the right way to imagine and name God. "He" will be mediated to her through words, images, stories, and myths shaped, written, and spoken by men. She will adopt the god she is given. It is too dangerous to rebel. If she dares to venture out of the lines by communing with the spirit of a tree, the mysterious night sky, or her grandma, she will be labeled heretic, backslider, or witch. She is told:

Prideful One, Your grandma is not God; neither is your favorite star or rock. God has only one name and one face. You shall have no gods before him. God is Father, Son, and Holy Ghost. He is found in the church, in the heavens, in the holy book, not in you. God is the God of Abraham, Isaac, and Jacob. He is God of the fathers and sons, the daughters have no say in the matter. Remember: As it was in the beginning, it is now and ever shall be.

The Spirit-Filled One falls asleep. Occasionally she awakens to remind the girl-child-turned-woman of what she once knew. These periodic reminders are painful. The woman fills her life with distractions so she will not hear the quiet inner voice, calling her to return home to her own spirituality. Years later, new teachers enter the woman's life—a therapist, a self-help group, a women's support circle, or a beloved friend. They remind her of what she once knew:

Spirit-Filled One, Your grandma is God and so are your favorite star and rock. God has many names and many faces. God is Mother, Daughter, and Wise Old Crone. She is found in your mothers, in your daughters, and in you. God is the God of Sarah and Hagar, of Leah and Rachel. She is Mother of All Living, and blessed are her daughters. You are girl-woman made in her image. The spirit of the universe pulsates through you. Be full of yourself. You are good. You are very good.

The Unbeliever's Guide to Spirituality

We had no choice. Belief in the Judeo-Christian God was expected, compulsory like wearing dresses and saying "I'm sorry." Although compulsory, it wasn't natural. We are born without belief in God.

INTRODUCTION   *Gods, Goddesses, and Higher Powers*

CHAPTER 1   *Compulsory Belief in God*
    Dismantling the Idolatry of God the Father
    Moving Beyond Gender, Moving Beyond God

CHAPTER 2   *A Historical Connection: Re-writing the Scripture*
    Dismantling Tradition
    Our Bodies, Lives, and Relationships as Sacred Text

CHAPTER 3   *An Inner Connection: Re-directing Prayer and Meditation*
    Dismantling Hierarchy
    Prayer as Breath, Prayer as Conversation
    Meditation as Silence, Meditation as Listening

CHAPTER 4   *A Communal Connection: Re-assigning Accountability*
    Dismantling the Throne of God
    Sin as Self-Criticism, Salvation as Self-Celebration
    Sin as Isolation, Salvation as Connection

CHAPTER 5   *An Organic Connection: Re-uniting Life and Death, Darkness and Light*
    Dismantling Duality
    Dispensing with Threats and Promises
    Darkness as Essential, Death as Possibility

CHAPTER 6   *A Creative Connection: Re-framing Life Passages*
    Dismantling Conformity
    The Rituals and Ceremonies of Ordinary Life

Dismantling the Throne of God

As we dismantle the throne of God, we must reformulate traditional religion's answers to the fundamental questions of human existence from our own experience as women. As the image of the big guy in the heavens scrutinizing our every thought and action dissolves, and as his system of rewards and punishments keeping us in line is disbanded, women are redefining sin, salvation, and surrender.

Ascent has been the journey of men. They erect ladders and monuments, reaching toward the heavens. They name their gods "Higher Power" and "God of the High Places." They have accurately defined their sin as pride, the willful pursuit of power, and the desire to be like God. In a society that worships a male God, these have not been our sins. Godlikeness has never been an option for us. Our place has been secondary and supportive.

The root of our sin has been an alienation from ourselves and an accompanying self-critical spirit. We have internalized carefully designed systems of thought and belief that take for granted our defectiveness and inferiority. We sin by our own participation in a paradigm that is not woman- or life-affirming and by our cooperation in the maintenance of this paradigm in the training of our daughters and granddaughters.

We sin each time we ask the question "what's wrong with me;" each time we waste our time, money, and energy on a frantic search for remedies; each time we twist ourselves out of shape in response to an "expert" opinion. We sin when we hide our bodies beneath layers of clothing, our natural processes beneath layers of secrecy, our sexuality beneath layers of passivity, our opinions and thoughts beneath layers of conformity, and our feelings beneath layers of restraint. We sin when we hide the reality of our lives beneath layers of seething resentment in response to and in avoidance of the persistent scrutiny of the culture, of God, and eventually, of ourselves.

As we redefine sin we rethink the remedies put forward to alleviate our sinful condition. Men's sins have been pride and grandiosity, therefore ego deflation, denial of self, and "surrender to God's will" have been appropriate remedies. Our two-fold sin of alienation from self and an all-consuming self-critical attitude require a conversion of sorts. We turn inward—instead of looking to gods and higher powers outside of our lives for salvation, we journey "home" to ourselves. Instead of ascending to enlightened states of being that involve the denial of the self, we discover that ours is a journey of descent—we look deep within to reclaim forgotten aspects of ourselves.

In our descent we reach beneath our obsession with flaws, beneath the accomplishments that mask our sense of unworthiness, beneath years of alienation from ourselves, toward the goodness at our center. As we embrace our original goodness our inner spaces are cleared out and reclaimed as our own. No longer scrutinizing every facet of our beings to figure out what is wrong, we celebrate ourselves as powerful and gifted children of life. We find rest within our own lives and accept all of ourselves as worthy.

Something Old, Something New

Several high school and college-aged young women told their stories on *Oprah!* the other day. Caught in the life-threatening swirls of possessive, jealous, and controlling boyfriends, they represent, according to statistics, one out of every four American young women. Whirling in a chaos not their own, unable to get their bearings, some had lost years of their lives—important, irreplaceable years.

While their classmates were testing the limits of their intellectual capacities and exploring their interests and curiosities to discern a direction, a calling, a career, a focus for their astounding life energy and potential, these young women lost all interest in themselves, their friends, their studies, and their futures. They told us about the contraction of their lives to meet the demands, to fulfill the expectations, and to obey the dictates of their jealous lovers:

"He tells me who I can see and who I can't see."

"I have to check in with him on the hour or he gets angry."

"He broke my pager so no one else can contact me."

"He wants me to dress a certain way based on his preferences. I have no choice in the matter."

"If another boy talks to me, he holds me responsible. He is very jealous. I can't have male friends."

I was horrified as they told their stories. How can this be in 1999, when Madeline Albright is negotiating humanitarian interventions and peace agreements around the world, when the players of the Women's National Basketball Association are inspiring a generation of Title IX young women, and when Oprah herself is offering women and girls transformational resources daily on national TV? How can this be in so-called post-feminist America where we're told all the battles have been won and true gender equality is at hand?

Oprah asked the resident "expert" my question. She reminded the audience that one out of four adult women is in an abusive relationship—like mother, like daughter. More profoundly, young women in our culture are convinced by the age of twelve that the pursuit and maintenance of a relationship with a man should be their number one priority, a priority that can easily turn into an obsession with life-threatening consequences. How can this be and yet there it was, poignantly portrayed on national TV—one out of four young women were facing the same old challenges in 1999 as their counterparts had in 1969, 1959, 1949.

One young women didn't make it to *Oprah!* to tell her story. Instead her father told viewers about the night she was picked up by her boyfriend. They drove to his apartment for a "breaking up" ritual, returning each other's CDs and other valuable items exchanged during their relationship. This sweet young woman believed they could remain friends, right up until her final breath. With "If I can't have you, no one else will," her life was stolen by a possessive lover. Her precious spirit lives on in her father's ministry among young women and men. He tells his daughter's story. He hopes some lives are saved in memory of her.

Imagine an adolescence in which our daughters, granddaughters, and nieces deepen their relationship to their natural vitality, resilience, and sense of self. Imagine our young women growing in knowledge and love of themselves. Young women vowing faithfulness to their own lives and capacities. Young women remaining loyal to themselves, regardless.

Imagine a girl-affirming rite of passage, a ceremony of commitment to themselves, culminating with these words of self-blessing: "No more waiting. This is it. This is my life. Nothing to wait for. Nowhere else to go. No one to make it all different. This is it. What a relief to have finally landed—here, now. Blessed be my life!"

Space for the Unknown

I offered a workshop in New York City, surrounding women with images of the divine feminine and reflecting on the influence of these images on their bodies, relationships, and self-understanding. Using sacred drama, image-making, movement meditation, healing ritual, and creative group interaction, we encountered the stories of women gathered from the margins of history and religion, including Eve, the Mother of All Living; Lilith, the Rebellious First Woman; Mary, the Queen of Heaven; The One Who Shed Her Blood; The Wounded Healers, and The Wise Old Woman.

Afterward Sharon, a diversity trainer, shared her discomfort: "I believe it is important to move beyond gender in our understanding of God to bring men and women together rather than to divide them." Her colleague was listening to our conversation and responded to her, "You sound like the critics of affirmative action we interact with everyday in our diversity work. They say, 'Let's move beyond all this color stuff. We live in a color-blind society.' And you and I know that color-blind means the same old white dominance and privilege because there isn't a level playing field yet." "That's right," I continued, "and there isn't a level playing field in the heavens yet either." Sharon got it and smiled a knowing smile.

We avoid two essential and potentially uncomfortable steps when we move prematurely to a genderless sense of the divine. First of all, we must dismantle the idolatry of God the father in our societies, churches, and families, *and* within ourselves. And secondly, we must encounter the divine feminine to restore our personal and collective balance. Yes, just as it is necessary to dismantle racism and its personal and systemic consequences before affirmative action programs are set aside, so it is necessary to dethrone the male God and invite the exiled feminine to take her rightful place beside him, before we consider moving to a genderless sense of the divine.

And even then it may not be possible, or even desirable, to eradicate all images of the divine. As a human community we have always employed our imaginations to give shape, form, and meaning to our noblest visions. This is a tenacious human impulse. Rather than eliminating all names and images in an artificial attempt to be "spiritually correct," imagine services and ceremonies that begin with an inclusive invocation, welcoming many names of the divine:

Let us bring many names, always mindful that the ultimate truth, wisdom, and mystery of the Universe is far deeper, higher, wider, and richer than any name or image we use to refer to it. Let us bring many names into this sacred space, and no names at all.

Bring many names…moving us beyond the limitations of gender: Deeper Wisdom, Higher Power, Wise Energy, Source of Life, Community of Support, Sacred Breath.

Bring many names…retaining the relational quality of the divine: Loving Wise One, Welcoming Friend, Compassionate One, Nurturing One, Counselor, Seeker of the Lost.

Bring many names…weaving traditional names into an unfolding spirituality: Loving Father; Abba; Jesus; Holy Spirit; Mother-Father God; Creator, Redeemer, and Sustainer.

Bring many names…challenging the idolatry of traditional religion: Goddess, Woman God, Sister God, Sophia, A God With Breasts Like Mine, Mother of All Living.

Bring many names and no names at all. In the silence let us leave space for the unknown.

On Your Anniversary

Looking Back

Honor the years you bring to this day. Laughter and tears, births and deaths, joy and sorrow—the fullness of life is held within your shared years. Take this moment to honor your tenacious choice to share life with each other.

Celebrate your faithfulness to each other. Day in and day out, in tender times and in awkward situations, in flowing times and in seasons of stagnation, in fullness and emptiness, in fear and in courage, in trouble and in beauty, you have remained faithful to your relationship. Take this moment to celebrate your choice to love.

Remember you've always found your way to the other side of each challenge. No matter the nature of the challenge, you have found a way, you have sought the support, you have discovered the insight, you have gone the extra mile, you have listened more deeply, you have found the strength to forgive, to love, to show mercy, to tell the truth...over and over again. Take this moment to remember your choice to keep loving.

Honor the beauty of your relationship. You have chosen the way of shared independence. You are two individuals, separate and unique in feeling, thinking, and experience. You each bring to this day a colorful solitude: friends, hobbies, and interests of your own. You have chosen a relationship that encourages your distinct identities. Take this moment to appreciate your choice to love each other's individuality, to honor the distinct shape of each other's thoughts, feelings, and experiences of life.

Looking Ahead: Daily Choices

What we turn our energy and attention toward grows. What we withdraw our energy and attention from dissolves. Your mission, should you choose to accept it, is to deepen your intimacy by choosing to live in the present. From this day forward bless the past, surrender the future, and live fully in the present—always returning to the present, to being present, to offering full heart, mind, and body presence to your partner.

Choose to bless the past. Bless the past by fasting from complaints about it and from rehearsal of its insults and injuries. From this day forward speak only words of gratitude about the past. Let us pause to bless the past: "The past has been our teacher, healer, and challenge. We are grateful it has escorted us to this day." And so it is.

Choose to surrender all anxiety about the future. Anxiety about an unknown future is a futile use of life energy. It removes us from this present moment. Let us pause to let go of our anxiety: "We surrender our anxiety and leave space for the unknown—a peaceful space within our hearts and minds that knows all is well, here and now." And so it is.

Choose to live fully in this day. This moment is the gift of life. Life is supremely efficient. It gives us everything we need to live fully in this moment. With a conscious breath we return to this moment when we wander away from it. The breath from which all life unfolds. The breath in which past, present, and future meet. Let us receive the gift of life: "We choose to live fully in this day. To stand in awe of it. To frolic in it with those we love. To rest in the arms of life as it unfolds one moment at a time." And so it is.

Looking Ahead: Daily Rituals
What we turn our energy and attention toward grows. What we withdraw our energy and attention from dissolves. Your mission, should you choose to accept it, is to deepen your intimacy by developing new habits of togetherness. From this day forward turn toward each other regularly by setting time aside for a three-part ritual of blessing.

Celebrate Yourself. Turn away from self-criticism, self-pity, and self-complaint. Turn toward the gifted, loving, and capable person you are by sharing one self-celebration. Yes, love and celebrate yourself *out loud* in the presence of your partner.

Appreciate Each Other. Turn away from the words and actions of your partner that you scrutinize and criticize. Turn toward the words and actions of your partner you appreciate by sharing one of them. Yes, appreciate your partner *out loud* every day.

Acknowledge Your Gratitude. Turn your attention away from criticism and complaint about life. Turn your attention toward the blessing and goodness of life by sharing one gratitude. Yes, share your gratitude for life *out loud* in the presence of your partner.

Imagine lovers who share a spiritual practice of silence and reflection to stay in alignment with the essence of their love. Gratitude for All That Is fills their relationship. And so it is!

In the Fullness of Time

A camper noticed a moth pushing, straining, and struggling to get out of its cocoon. It was a disturbing sight. When she could take it no longer, she extended the tiny slit-opening of the cocoon. The moth was freed. It fell to the ground and died. The camper was devastated. Her intention had been to help.

Inspired by the story, I investigated the moth's life. Its life cycle from egg to adult moth is orchestrated by a remarkable inner mechanism of "right timing," allowing for the emergence of the larva to coincide with an adequate food supply, for the outgrowing of each of its skins, for the location and creation of the cocoon, for the length of its state of lethargy, and for its emergence as a fully formed adult moth when conditions are adequate for its survival.

The struggle against the walls of the cocoon supports the moth's metamorphosis by strengthening its wings and releasing fluids to enhance its coloring. The camper, unaware of the trustworthiness of timing and the sacredness of struggle in the moth's cycle, cut open the cocoon. This premature release led to the death of the moth. Swirling in her own discomfort, she intruded in the moth's life process. Yet the moth was content in the midst of its own trustworthy process, a process essential to its development.

Like the moth, each of us is an emerging healthy adult whose process is orchestrated by a finely tuned inner timing. In the fullness of time, when a behavior begins to hamper, press, and squeeze us, we twist and turn until we burst out of the old skin and are freed at a deeper level of our existence. Each time a memory or feeling is ready to be acknowledged out of decades of denial, it gnaws its way to the surface through a dream or a sensory memory, through a movie, or by reading the stories of others. In the fullness of time, it is remembered or felt. The trustworthy timing of our Inner Wisdom leads us to each new transformation when we are ready.

Awakenings

In the Very Beginning

In the very beginning of her life the girl-child loves herself. She moves through each day with an exuberant strength, a remarkable energy, and a contagious liveliness. Her days are meaningful and unfold according to a deep wisdom that resides within her. It faithfully orchestrates her movements from crawling to walking to running; her sounds from garbles to single words to sentences; and her knowing of the world through her sensual connection to it.

Her purpose is clear: to live fully in the abundance of her life. With courage, she explores her world. Every experience is filled with wonder and awe. It is enough to gaze at the redness of an apple; to watch the water flow over the rocks in a stream; to listen to the rain dance; to count the peas on her plate. Ordinary life is her teacher, her challenge, and her delight.

She says a big *yes* to Life as it pulsates through her body. With excitement, she explores her body. She is unafraid of channeling strong feelings through her. She feels her joy, her sadness, her anger, and her fear. She is pregnant with her own life. She is content to be alone. She touches the depths of her uniqueness. She loves her mind. She likes herself when she looks in the mirror.

She trusts her vision of the world and expresses it. With wonder and delight, she paints a picture, creates a dance, and makes up a song. To give expression to what she sees is as natural as her breathing. And when challenged, she is not lost for words. She has a vocabulary to speak about her experience. She speaks from her heart. She voices her truth. She has no fear, no sense that to do it her way is wrong or dangerous.

She is a warrior. It takes no effort for her to summon up her courage, to arouse her spirit. With her courage, she solves problems. She is capable of carrying out any task that confronts her. She has everything she needs within the grasp of her mind and her imagination. She accomplishes great things in her mind, in her room, and in the neighborhood. With her spirit, she changes what doesn't work for her. She says "I don't like that person" when she doesn't, and "I like that person" when she does. She says *no* when she doesn't want to be hugged. She takes care of herself.

A Reversal of Value

Over time, the inner voice that led her into wonder-filled explorations is replaced by critical voices. As a result, the girl-child's original vision is narrowed; she sees the world as everyone else sees it. She loses her ability to act spontaneously; she acts as expected. Her original trust in herself is shattered; she waits to be told how to live. Her original spunk is exiled; she learns that it is dangerous to venture outside the lines. Her original goodness is labeled unnatural-unfeminine-too intense-evil by the adults in her life.

While in seminary, I read a Kierkegardian parable that reminds me of the sad reversals of childhood.

In the dark of the night thieves entered a store and did their work. In the morning the store opened at the appointed time. It was obvious to the clerk that the store had been entered and yet nothing seemed to have been taken. As the day progressed and customers brought merchandise to the counter, the storekeepers began to notice a curious phenomenon. The merchandise of least value wore the tags of greatest value. And the items of greatest value carried the tags of least value. By the end of the day the puzzle had been solved. The thieves had reversed the price tags.

Sadly, a conformity-based childhood reverses the price tags: The natural and essential self, a priceless treasure, is demeaned and set aside, and the artificial and constructed self grows in value. Image is more valuable than essence; conformity more priceless than originality; and lies are celebrated as truth. Throughout childhood we are faced with a challenging dilemma: to tell the truth and be who we are, risking abandonment and rejection, or to conform by developing an artificial self to win the approval of important adults and to survive childhood.

The Veil of Shame

Throughout the development of Western civilization, women were expected to wear shame like a garment, a covering, a veil to remind them of their inferiority and their proper place in the hierarchic scheme of things, and to protect others from the peril and temptation of their unveiled presence. Shame was considered an essential female characteristic. Shame kept women in line.

Shame was to be demonstrated in a woman's behavior: A virtuous woman was silent, chaste, obedient, discreet, shy, restrained, timid, and passive. It was to be displayed in a woman's appearance: A virtuous woman lowered her head and her eyes to avoid direct eye contact with men, blushed to acknowledge the embarrassment of being female, covered her head to indicate her subordination to her husband's authority, and covered her body to protect men from the peril of her natural seductiveness.

Shame was to be illustrated in the amount of space a woman occupied: A virtuous woman made herself small to fit into the scheme of things. Her feelings remained quiet and acceptable; her thoughts, tame and unthreatening; her needs, silent and nonexistent; her appetites, manageable. A virtuous woman took up very little space with her body. She was and still is in danger of disappearing.

Shameless women refused to stay in line. They were condemned for their audacity to refuse "B" status and their arrogance to step into "A" status beside men. They were damned for exhibiting the unbecoming qualities of immodesty and personal ambition, and for upsetting the divine order of things. In second-century Rome, the humiliation of an unfaithful wife was made into a public spectacle. She was paraded nude on a donkey into the town center, vulnerable to the glaring crowd's insults and mockery. A sexually autonomous woman was without shame and could not be tolerated.

In the third century the church father Epiphanius railed against the "heretical" Montanist sect because the women among them claimed Eve as their champion and assumed leadership roles, ignoring the differences of nature:

They bring with them many useless testimonies, attributing a special grace to Eve because she first ate of the tree of knowledge. Women among them are bishops, presbyters, and the rest, as if there were no difference of nature, even if the women among them were ordained to the episcopacy and presbyterate because of Eve, they hear the Lord saying: "Your orientation will be toward your husband and he shall rule over you." The apostolic saying escaped their notice, namely that: "Man is not from woman but woman from the man"; and "Adam was not deceived, but Eve was first deceived into transgression." Oh, the multifaceted error of this world!

A literal and figurative veil of shame has been passed from one generation of women to another, reminding us always to bear in mind, heart, and body our proper place in the scheme of things. The veiling is for our own good, our mothers told us in word and action. They know what happens to women who step outside the lines—to shameless women who refuse to hide their creativity, intelligence, physical strength, ambition, and sexuality. Be careful, dear, the world doesn't like uppity women. They are called names: witch, ball buster, bitch, man hater, bra burner, old maid, whore, spinster, selfish, ambitious. They are ostracized, remember Eve. They are burned, remember the witches. They are stoned, remember the woman caught in adultery. They are exiled, remember the rebellious first woman, Lilith. They are locked up, remember poor Grandma. They grow old alone, remember old maid Aunt Matilda. Women who are full of themselves meet with an awful end.

What's Wrong with Me?

We frequent the therapist's office,
hoping the past holds an answer within it.

We fill the churches,
maybe God knows the answer.

We attend self-help meetings,
assured an answer is encoded within the Twelve Steps.

We write "Dear Abby" and every other expert,
certain that they must know the answer.

We sit at the feet of spirituality gurus,
believing they will show us the way to an answer.

We buy every self-help book that hits the market,
confident that a new project will quiet the question.

We consent to outrageous measures
to guarantee our fertility or our attractability,
convinced that the presence of a child
or a lover in our arms will dissolve the question.

We sign up for diet clubs and plans and spas,
convinced that our bodies are at the core of the answer,
whatever it turns out to be.

We spend hundreds of dollars
on new outfits to hide the question
and on new body parts to eradicate the question.

And then at night after the day's search is over,
we binge on a quart of ice cream or a bottle of wine,
or we spend hours on the Internet or telephone
in tormented conversations trying to figure out

why the current relationship isn't working,
hoping that when we reach the bottom of the quart or bottle,
or the far reaches of the internet or conversation,
things will have shifted deep within us
and once and for all we will know the answer
and what to do about it.

Yet no matter what we do in search of an answer:
no matter how much we lose or how slimming the dress,
no matter how expensive or authoritative the expert,
no matter how many babies, relationships,
possessions we have or don't have,
no matter how spiritual, therapeutic, or recovered we become,
we are left with the same question over and over again
as we look into the mirror horrified
that the restructuring of our relationship, our womb,
or our breasts did not quiet the question
there it is in the morning whispering from the mirror,
"What's wrong with me? What's wrong with me?"
A mantra that accompanies us the length of our days.

Bittersweet Legacy

The influence of family and religion are intertwined in my experience and their legacy has been bittersweet. The Methodist Church we attended in my early childhood provided a respite for my mother and her daughters. We were happiest in the church, away from the escapades of my violent alcoholic father. He couldn't hurt us while we were in the church. And yet the minister encouraged my mother to return to her husband; to love, honor, and obey him no matter the cost to her, or to us.

The Catholic orphanage of my elementary school years became my surrogate family. There were nuns who inspired me to dance, to sing, and to learn; nuns, like Sister Joan of Arc, who supported my potential for health and fullness. There were others who lined us up for regular paddlings or locked us in dark storerooms for hours on end. Their sarcastic words and demeaning actions lingered in my self-image for many years. The priest was God at the orphanage, and he was given special privileges. There was no place to go to get away from God and his representatives. No private place where they couldn't find me.

The non-denominational, inter-racial church of adolescence and young adulthood was kind and generous to my mother and her two young daughters as we reunited in the big city of Newark, New Jersey. They provided food, clothes, and ongoing support as we attempted to create a family after several years of separation. The church offered me remarkable opportunities to develop my talents—all within the narrow confines of fundamentalism. Hundreds of city kids, most from single-parent homes, were involved in our youth group, the Conquerors Club. Supported by the church, many of us went on to Christian colleges, and some, on to graduate school and seminary. The male professors and ministers groomed me to be articulate and persuasive, and yet there was no room for me in their religious world except as minister's wife or assistant. Only the boys could be world changers. Only the boys could be ministers and preach.

Although there were many individual acts of kindness offered to me and to my family by the nuns, priests, and ministers of my early years, they were overshadowed by the image of a male God who expected perfection and who held me personally responsible for the death of his only begotten son and for the salvation of the world. I do not remember one religious experience until I was thirty that celebrated me without any conditions. Religion celebrated God's love for me in spite of my sinfulness. Religion celebrated God's forgiveness of me in spite of my participation in the death of Christ.

I did not receive one pure unqualified celebration of my life—it was a gift from God and could be taken away at any moment; of my body—it was to be mistrusted, controlled, and neuterized; of my thoughts—they were like wayward children, prone to selfishness and impurity; of my feelings—they were to be crucified with Christ; of my gifts—they were God's gifts channeled through me and I was to take no credit for them. Sadly, the conversion I experienced, in God's name, required that I turn away from my natural sensations, needs, desires, and capacities and turn toward a male God who would live "his" life through me.

Suicide

The final recourse is suicide
successfully attempted
by many women throughout the ages.
The ultimate choice to transcend
the weakness
the responsibility
the harassment
of being female.

The way out of it all, the final relinquishment,
to die in one dramatic moment
of courage and willfulness
or to slowly disappear
under layers of fat,
in a drug-induced stupor,
or in the vagueness of an unformed life.

Palladius traveled through Egypt in the fourth century
to gather anecdotal tales of holy women and men.
He records the story of Alexandra.

*A maidservant named Alexandra left the city and immured herself in a
tomb. She received the necessities of life through a window, and for ten
years never looked a woman or man in the face.*

*Melanie told us that she beheld Alexandra face to face, standing near her
window, and asked her to tell why she had immured herself in a tomb.
She told Melanie: "A man was distracted in mind because of me, and
rather than scandalize a soul made in the image of God, I betook myself
alive to a tomb, lest I seem to cause him suffering or reject him."*

*When Melanie asked her how she perseveres, never seeing anyone, and
battling against weariness, Alexandra said: "From early dawn to the*

ninth hour I pray from hour to hour while spinning flax. The rest of the time I go over in my mind the holy patriarchs, prophets, apostles, and martyrs. Then I eat my crusts and wait patiently for my end with good hope."

In the tenth year she fell asleep after she had arranged herself. The woman who used to go to her received no answer and announced this to us. Breaking open the door, we entered and found her dead.

Some women are murdered
by the words absorbed into their life stream.
Like the steady drip of an IV inserted at birth
the words of the holy patriarchs, prophets, apostles, and martyrs
are responsible for Alexandra's death.
Their words held her body
responsible for the distraction of men.
Their words slowly poisoned her
as they praised her virtue
for successfully surpassing the weakness of being female.
May she rest in peace.

Idolatry

To fully understand our communal history we must explore religion's pivotal role in the development of Western civilization's historical, philosophical, theological, and psychological viewpoints. Origen, an Alexandrian Church Father, wrote these words in the third century: "What is seen with the eyes of the Creator is masculine, and not feminine, for God does not stoop to look upon what is feminine and of the flesh." Clearly, the architects of Western civilization attributed the male gender to the divine, supporting their notions of the superiority of the male—he looks like God and is looked at by God, and the inferiority of the female—she does not look like God and he does not stoop so low as to look at her.

"What's the big deal about the gender of God?" is the question I have considered with audiences all over the country in bookstores, churches, and women's centers, and on radio and television interview and call-in programs. We consider the question in response and reaction to a performance piece-reading entitled "Imagine" based on my first book. The piece invites audiences to imagine how their lives might have been different surrounded by images of the divine feminine in the churches, synagogues, and homes of childhood. Through performances and presentations, and through my ministry, writing, and life, I challenge the human community to confront its idolatry of God the father.

The responses I have received illustrate the pervasive influence of the male god-image and the dangers of stepping outside the lines to question, reject, and redesign religion from our perspective as women. In Salt Lake City, Mormon men expressed outrage that women would even consider naming and imagining their own gods: "a blasphemous enterprise" was one caller's response. A Utah Sunday School teacher and his class became concerned after reading an interview in a local paper. They sent me a stack of letters, inviting me to "come back to father God." The teacher rebuked me for encouraging women to create gods in their own image and likeness. "Lay down your pride and leave God alone" was his message to me.

In Albuquerque, conservative Christian women and men called with similar outrage, name-calling, and concern that I find my way back to the one true God. In Hayward, California, the callers criticized the station for allowing such a blasphemous discussion to be aired. An Oakland caller assured me that her church would pray for my wayward soul. In response to a Boulder magazine interview, a flurry of letters attacked anyone who would question the male God of traditional religion. A Colorado man labeled our search for a God who looks like us "narcissistic feminism," an interesting comment given the tenacity with which men have safeguarded the image of the male God for the past 4,000 years.

"God is male and that's a fact" sums up the response of many women and men in this country. The gender of God is a *big deal.* "His" image and likeness have been woven into the history, philosophy, religion, and psychology that trickle down to us through the ages, a legacy passed on from generation to generation in the unexamined beliefs, customs, and preferences of a society that worships a male God and offers particular privileges to those who look like him. God the father has remained an undisturbed idol for too long.

The Old Ways

There have always been women who remember the old ways.
Women who hold within them
the memory of a time
in the very beginning
when women were honored.

Women who refuse
to worship the gods,
to learn the language,
to take the names
of the fathers.

Women who refuse to twist
their female bodies out of shape,
to fit into definitions,
to transcend limitations.
Women who love their bodies. Regardless.

Women who refuse to please others
by becoming smaller than they are.
Women who take up space
with their thoughts and feelings,
their needs and desires,
their anger and their dreams.

Loud and strong
women from every age,
wild women, spinster women,
wise women, rebellious women,
women who love women,
midwives, witches, healers, activists.

Banners and placards aloft...

Eve, the Mother of All Living
Take and eat of the good fruit of life. Take a big bite!

Sappho
She Who Gives Birth Has Power Over Life and Death.

Mary Wollstonecraft
Break the Silken Fetters.

Sojourner Truth
Ain't I a Woman!

Margaret Sanger
Speak and Act in Defiance of Convention.

Elizabeth Cady Stanton
*Whatever the Bible may be made to do in Hebrew and Greek
in plain English it does not exalt and dignify women.*

Karen Horney
Womb Envy Is More Like It.

Audre Lorde
The Master's Tools Will Never Dismantle the Master's House.

One by one they commit the forbidden act
of biting into patriarchal thought,
refuting it, smashing it,
discarding it, and beginning again
in the very beginning when women
loved their bodies,
named their gods,
authored their lives
when women refused to surrender
except to life as it pulsated through them.

Women reminding us
there is nothing wrong
there never has been anything wrong
there never will be anything wrong
with woman
that's why nothing ever works.
Stop asking the question!

One by one they speak the truth of a woman's life
told with heart, mind, and body
refusing dissection,
they are women and poets and theorists,
who gather our brokenness
into their words
an impulse toward wholeness
awakens within us
and we become again
as we once were
whole.

Outrageous Words

Some of us missed the second wave of feminism. We were immersed in fundamentalistic traditions that kept us isolated from the political movements in the wider culture. We were dealing with the aftermath of growing up in severely dysfunctional homes, the kind of home situations no one wanted to hear about because they were so "depressing." We were struggling with our addictions to food, drugs, alcohol, and relationships. Addictions that kept us comatose, numbed out until we were ready to walk through our personal pasts. Or we were immersed in the isolation of being Mrs. Somebody, as fearful of those angry feminist "bra burners" as our husbands were.

Our consciousness raising came much later than our feminist sisters. The "knight in shining armor" mythology shattered as we found ourselves divorced and the sole financial and emotional providers for our children. We sought support at a local women's center and began to listen to women's stories, shedding the competitive attitudes of a lifetime. We stumbled into a self-help meeting and a woman said "Goddess" instead of the compulsory "God" in the Twelve Steps, and we wondered how she got the courage to commit such a heretical act. Our therapist suggested we read *The Second Sex* or *The Creation of Patriarchy,* and we were stunned that women were writing such powerful treatises and that we knew nothing about them. We showed up at seminary to major in religious education, the appropriate focus for young women, only to discover most of our classmates were "radical" women going into the ordained ministry. We relocated and found ourselves drawn to the local Unitarian church. We sat with tears in our eyes every Sunday listening to the preacher. *Her* words resonated with our deepest experience in a way that the words of male ministers had never been able to do.

It is always in the company of women that we are reminded of our common heritage as women. A heritage that reaches beyond "the beginning" defined by men to the "very beginning" when the divine was imagined as woman. We discover that we are surrounded by a courageous cloud of witnesses whose experience and stories, ideas and images, creativity and outrage become healing resources for us. No longer asking, "What's wrong with me?," we are freed from our obsession with the works, words, and lives of men. Self-possessed, we step outside of patriarchal thought and immerse ourselves in women's history, philosophy, theology, creativity, and spirituality. We receive Gerda Lerner's challenge:

Perhaps the greatest challenge to thinking women is the challenge to move from the desire for safety and approval to the most "unfeminine" quality of all —that of intellectual arrogance, the supreme hubris which asserts to itself the right to reorder the world. The hubris of the godmakers, the hubris of the male system-builders.

We have been warned against exhibiting hubris all of our lives. Our feminist sisters support us to be arrogant for the salvation of our planet, out of balance and in danger of annihilating itself. In their every word, we hear the powerful affirmation, "It is right and good that you are woman. Be full of yourself!"

Loving Our Bodies—Regardless

My early work among women as director of Circle of Life Women's Center flowed from my own need to critically distance from, examine, and dismantle the unexamined intellectual, theological, psychological, and personal paradigms that had shaped my self-understanding as a woman and my chronic self-criticism. I designed woman-affirming filters with which to sort through each arena, discarding what was harmful and incorporating what was woman-affirming into the fabric of our transformative perspective. Along the way I developed supportive rituals, sacred texts, and communal experiences to breathe life into our woman-affirming understanding of ourselves and each other. Together we journeyed from self-criticism to self-celebration.

In this current season of my life I discovered a disturbing layer of unaddressed body-criticism within myself and noticed an intensification of body-violence within the community of women. Women of all ages are doing violence to their bodies and injuring their natural body-intelligence and body-shape. Choosing to treat one's body violently through repeated bingeing/starving diet cycles, obsessive exercise regimens, life-threatening starvation, or cosmetic surgery has become customary and even celebrated among American women.

We are outraged by the ancient custom of foot binding and by the current awareness of genital mutilation, and yet in record numbers we are choosing to have our breasts cut open and augmented, our noses broken and reshaped, our wrinkles injected with collagen, our faces manipulated and peeled, and our bodies exercised and starved to death. Self-loathing trickles down from generation to generation. Mothers, grandmothers, aunts, counselors, and teachers, supported by this image-based/woman-scrutinizing/age-phobic society, pass on the necessity of ornamentalism, the tyranny of the scale, the fear of food, and the dread of aging to our daughters.

When our desire to be "fit" is motivated by the culture's images of beauty and by our own critical self-scrutiny we are unable to sustain health and fitness because the image is unreachable. We will never be perfect enough, pretty enough, or fit enough. We will never be able to arrest the shifts and changes that accompany the organic process of aging. On the other hand, when we react to the culture's images of beauty and "fitness" by refusing to take care of ourselves inspired by a distorted interpretation of feminism or a misapplied critique of the culture's assault, we hurt our bodies and jeopardize our health.

To support women to love their bodies through the seasons of life, I developed *The WOW! Intensive*—an essence- and purpose-based program for women who are ready:

- ∴ to let go of their belief in personal powerlessness, and embrace personal responsibility for the health and fitness of their body, mind, and spirit;
- ∴ to let go of the habit of scrutinizing their body and image, and embrace a new focus: cultivation of essence and expression of purpose;
- ∴ to let go of the chronic criticism of their body, age, and self, and embrace a self-loving attitude expressed in reverent words and respectful actions;
- ∴ to let go of their patterns of inertia and self-sabotage, and embrace a daily commitment to disciplined action;
- ∴ to let go of the depleting repetition of old habits, and sustain mind, body, and spirit health through the seasons of life;
- ∴ to inspire and support the courage of their daughters and grand-daughters; nieces, parishioners, and clients to love their bodies, regardless.

Imagine a woman who believes her body is enough, just as it is. A woman who celebrates her body's rhythms and cycles as an exquisite resource. Who loves her body through the seasons of life—regardless. Imagine yourself as this woman.

Letter to the Editor

I was appalled by just about everything in the current issue of your magazine being marketed among teenage girls.

The Cover
Is His Love For Real? 50 Secret Signs
Never Get Dumped Again! We'll Tell You How
Extra: Your Intimate Beauty Horoscope
Banish Fat Days Forever; Mega Makeover

The Ten Categories of the Cover Girl Model Search
Beach Babe, Seriously Sexy,
Really Romantic, Majorly Mysterious,
Classy Cool, Way Dramatic,
Fierce Flirt, Nature Girl,
So Glamorous, Mega Modern

The Advertisements
Breast Boost Without Surgery: Silicone pads that look, feel, weigh, and even bounce like real breast. So natural they're undetectable.

Is it any wonder our daughters start asking the question "What's wrong with me?" by the time they are ten. Your magazine supports them to resent their own bodies as they scrutinize artificial images of models whose perfection is defined by a misogynistic culture and whose beauty is created by lights and make-up. Your magazine supports their growing urge to cover, starve, and violently alter their precious bodies. Numb and bored, our young women are waiting, often in front of a mirror, for a prince to come along and make their lives worth living.

For the sake of our daughters, change your message and your image. Support young women to know, love, and trust themselves. Support them to develop the full range of their human capacities. Support them to kiss sleeping beauty good-bye and awaken to their own lives. Include images of strong athletic women, supporting their bodies to develop organically. Include the words and images of intelligent women who refuse to twist their minds or bodies out of shape. Include the words and images of wise women with fully formed lives who refuse to set them aside to pursue men.

Imagine a young woman who has a fully-formed life. A young woman who doesn't set her life aside to pursue relationships. Who remains loyal to herself. Regardless.

Imagine a young woman who expresses herself clearly and directly. A young woman who has chosen an authentic existence. Who doesn't have time for "manipulative games."

Imagine a young woman in love with her own body. A young woman who believes her body is enough, just as it is. Who celebrates its rhythms and cycles as an exquisite resource.

The Journey Home

Sitting in a Twelve Step meeting, I listened as a woman spoke about trusting the God of her understanding: "When I let Higher Power take charge, everything works out fine. When I'm in the driver's seat, I blow it every time." Inspired by her talk, several other women acknowledged that they were fundamentally ill-equipped to deal with life. Based on their sense of inadequacy, they found it necessary to "surrender" to a power greater than themselves. Later that week I sat in a support circle as a woman complained about the unavailability of her therapist: "I have to see her every week or my life falls apart. I don't have what it takes to function without the assistance of a trained professional."

While on a book tour I was interviewed on a religious radio show. During the call-in part of the program, the inevitable question about sin and salvation was asked: "Do you believe we are sinners and in need of the salvation God offers?" I told the caller that my own inner wisdom was trustworthy and that it was communicated to me through my natural impulses, instincts, and intuition. I no longer needed the salvation offered by gods, higher powers, therapists, or gurus. The caller was appalled. "We can't trust ourselves," she exclaimed, "we are sinful and left to our own devices, we will mess things up every time. God is the only trustworthy one."

"You may not be able to trust yourself," I responded, "but I have learned to trust myself and so have the women with whom I sit in circle. We no longer expend our precious life energy scrutinizing every facet of our beings to figure out what's wrong with us. Instead, we celebrate ourselves as gifted and powerful children of life."

Yes, today I experience the trustworthiness of my natural impulses, instincts, and intuition. Trusted, they do not lead me to commit horrible acts of sin, to make self-destructive choices, or to fall into psychological waywardness. Rather, they blossom into life-affirming behaviors. Today I celebrate myself as an awe-inspiring child of life. It has been a long journey home.

Reversals

Our Mother

Our Mother, who art within us,
We celebrate your many names.
Your wisdom come. Your will be done,
Unfolding from the depths of us.

Each day you give us all that we need.
You remind us of our limits and we let go.
You support us in our power and we act with courage.

For you are the dwelling place within us,
the empowerment around us, and the celebration among us.
As it was in the very beginning, may it be now.

Exorcism

While studying at Princeton Seminary, I reread the Bible free of the fundamentalistic trappings of my adolescence. No longer fearful that I would be damned for tampering with "God's Word," I assumed equality with this very human book. I gathered the fragments of women's stories from my religious memory and from the margins of the text itself. I invited the women of old to visit my dreams and to tell me their names. I rewrote the stories I had most identified with during adolescence, changing the gender of the characters if necessary, inserting the specifics of my story into the text. I imagined Jesus as a Woman-Rabbi and Healer.

I found myself drawn again to the story of the man possessed by demons in Mark 5. At that time in my life, I felt possessed by "alien energies" in the form of childhood's critical words, images, experiences, and expectations. They had pursued me into adulthood and were dictating the terms of my existence. Raging within me, their force could no longer be contained.

I rewrote the biblical story (printed here in italics) and included the universal story of women of every age possessed of alien energies, deposited within us by the intellectual, philosophical, theological, and mythic traditions that assumed our inferiority and assaulted our bodies and lives (printed here in regular type). Two voices telling one story of women who acknowledge the past's influence on the present, who walk through the past to heal into the present, self-possessed and full of themselves!

A woman possessed by alien spirits had her dwelling among the tombs. She had often been fettered and chained up, but she had snapped her chains and broken the fetters. She could no longer be controlled; even chains were useless. No one was strong enough to master her. And so, unceasingly, night and day, she would cry aloud among the tombs and on the hillsides and cut herself with stones.

I see them in the distance. I watch them live out their days. They visit each other's homes. They converse in public places. They eat, live, and play together. They touch. It has been many years. I long to draw near. My eyes are weary from watching them at a distance, longing.

When she saw the Healer in the distance, she came out from among the tombs and ran and flung herself down before the Healer, shouting loudly, "What do you want with me, Healer? Do not torment me."

Hiding from a painful touch of long ago. The distance keeps me safe. It has become my friend. I cover my body. I watch it grow beneath the layers. No touch will penetrate the uncleanness of my being. My hands are tired of concealing my shame, hiding.

The Healer asked her, "What is your name?"
"My name is Legion," she said. "There are so many of us."
"Speak their names—one by one—and be healed."

Requires less nourishment. Incapable of governing her life. Passionate not rational. Bodily not soul-full. Weaker. Deformity of nature. Not equal in honor. Not equal in age. Easily deceived. Ruler of death and everything vile. Imperfect and ignoble. The beginning of transgression. Prone to vanity. The devil's gateway. The unsealer of the forbidden tree. Deserter of divine law. Destroyer of god's image. Responsible for Jesus' death. Perilous to all ages. Defective and misbegotten. Feeble in mind and body. Carnal. Necessary evil. Natural temptation. Evil of nature. Genitally deficient. Tomboyish. Unfeminine. Too sensitive-needy-fussy. Immodest. Impure. Fickle. Too intense. Inferior. Rude. Troublesome. Not good enough. Selfish and self-centered. Unhelpful. Big-headed. Self-inflated. Conceited.

The Healer addressed Legion, "Out, alien spirits, come out of this woman!" The Healer gave them leave; and the alien spirits came out, one by one. Exhausted, the woman fell to the ground. In the fullness of time, she awakened. The Healer asked her again, "What is your name?" "I am

Daughter of Woman," she answered. *"Rise up and go into the dark of the night,"* said the Healer. *"Go to the women. They will tell you the truth."*

I rise up and go into the night. In its darkness my eyes rest. The moon calls to me. She tells me of a time when women's lives were sacred. There were no shameful separations. She tells me of a time when women's bodies were honored. There were no painful touches.

My eyes closed, I find myself in a clearing of light with women from every age. Their song calls to me: "You who stand apart, come close. You who are out of touch, come near." They throw no stones, instead they offer me flowers and they touch me with healing and light. They sing to me: "It is right and good that you are woman."

Women from all ages, telling stories and dancing—in the light of the moon. In the stories, I hear my truth. In the dance, I shed my veil of shame. It is right and good that I am woman, that I am mad-woman.

The people came out to see what had happened. They saw the mad-woman who had been possessed by the legion of alien spirits, sitting there clothed in her right mind; and they were afraid. The spectators told them how the mad-woman had been cured.

As the Healer was leaving, the woman who had been possessed of alien spirits begged to go with her. The Healer would not allow it, but said to her, "Go home to your own folk and tell them that once you were divided against yourself and now you are whole."

The woman went off and spread the good news: "It is right and good that I am woman." And they were all amazed.

The Big Mama

In the very beginning was the Mother.

On the first day,
She gave birth to light and darkness.
They danced together.

On the second day,
She gave birth to land and water.
They touched.

On the third day,
She gave birth to green growing things.
They rooted and took a deep breath.

On the fourth day,
She gave birth to land, sea, and air creatures.
They walked, swam, and flew.

On the fifth day,
Her creation learned balance and cooperation.

On the sixth day,
She celebrated the creativity of all living things.

On the seventh day,
She left space for the unknown.

Eve, the Mother of All Living

I am Eve, the Mother of All Living, culmination of creation.
I hold and nurture life within me.
In the fullness of time I thrust and push life from me.
And all that I have given birth to is good, it is very good.

I was once known throughout the world as the Mother of All Living. The wisest among you have always honored me in your myths of beginnings. I have been called by many names, Fertile One Who Births All Things, the Great Mother, Law-Giving Mother, The Bearing One, She Who Gives Birth to the Gods, Queen of Heaven, True Sovereign, Mother of the World, Queen of the Stars. I was called Inanna in Ur; Ishtar in Babylon; Astarte in Phoenicia; Isis in Egypt; Womb Mother in Assyria; and Cerridwen among the Celts.

I was worshiped for many centuries before the God of the Hebrews was imagined into being. As men became threatened by my power and by my intimate involvement in the origins of all life, they swallowed my stories into their unfolding mythologies and twisted my truth. My original power and glory are hardly recognizable in the stories you heard in the churches, synagogues, and homes of your childhood. The image of Father God ordering the world into being was firmly imprinted on your imaginations. Did you even notice the absence of the Mother?

According to the Genesis myth, I was born of the man, from his rib they say. I am outraged at this twisting of the truth. Who among you was not nurtured in my womb? Who among you has forgotten the source of your life? Jehovah was ignorant of his mother. In his foolishness he said, "I am God. There is none beside me." His arrogance has always troubled me.

As the Mother of All Living, I exist before all things. From my body all that is proceeds. Every mother who bears a child is the embodiment of me. In her pregnancy, she holds and nurtures life within her. In her labor she thrusts life from her. She is woman, strong and powerful. She is the Mother of All Living. I am outraged that woman's good, strong body, containing all things necessary for life, and the body of Mother Earth, which receives back all good things to Herself, are objects of disgust and fear, to be controlled and dominated in the Genesis story.

I was given a pivotal role in men's developing mythology. They say that out of feminine weakness I ate the fruit and then seduced Adam. That I set in motion a series of events that resulted in our expulsion from the garden and the release of misery and death into the world.

They say I am guilty, and that evil is grounded in my very existence and nature. Of me was written, "From a woman was the beginning of sin and because of her we all die." For thirty centuries of Jewish and Christian history I have carried the burden of humankind's guilt and shame. No More!

Honor all that has been demeaned.
Receive all that has been cast aside.
The woman is good. She is very good.

In the very beginning the sacred grove was the birthplace of all things. Its trees of knowledge and life were intimately connected to my worship. They were not my private property, nor did I wish to control humankind's access to their wisdom. We honored the trees of the grove. We cared for them and caressed them. They held within them the secrets of life, the wisdom of the Earth and her seasons, and the awareness of sexuality.

Many Hebrews worshiped in my sacred groves. Hebrew women followed me. Some, in the secret of their hearts. Others boldly rejected Jehovah and convinced their husbands to follow me. When King Solomon grew old, his wives turned his heart toward the Goddess. He did not remain loyal to Jehovah as his father David had done. He built hill-shrines in my honor. The myth-makers twisted the truth to serve as a warning to the Hebrew people not to visit my sacred groves nor to eat of the fruit of its trees. And the most zealous of Jehovah's prophets cut down my groves and burned the bones of my priestesses.

To eat of the fruit of the tree was to eat of my flesh and drink of my life-giving fluid. In the woman Eve you catch glimpses of my former glory. She was intelligent, curious, eager, and strong. She ate of the fruit and received the wise secrets of life and the awareness of sexuality. For some this may be the forbidden fruit. For those of us who are Wisdom's daughters, it is a fruit of rare beauty and goodness.

Honor that which has been demeaned.
Receive all that has been cast aside.
The tree and its fruit are good. They are very good.

As the Mother of All Living, I pick the fruit of life. It is good and satisfies hunger. It is pleasant to the eye and offers pleasure. It is wise and opens the way to self-discovery and understanding.

Those among you who are curious, who lust for life in all its fluidity, dare with me. Bite into life and the fullness of its possibility. Believe in your goodness. Celebrate your goodness. Affirm the original goodness of your children and your children's children until the stories of old hold no power in their hearts.

I am Eve the Mother of All Living, culmination of creation.
I hold and nurture life within me.
In the fullness of time I thrust and push life from me.
And all that I have given birth to is good. It is very good.

Returning from Exile

The Kabbalistic tradition laments the exile of the feminine because the human community, bereft of the feminine, has access to only half of life's mercy, wisdom, strength, and blessing. I remembered this sentiment as I listened to a reporter stationed in Afghanistan describe the absence of women. He used the words "desolate" and "harsh" to describe a nation bereft of its women. He caught only glimpses of them. They were peripheral, hidden, and silenced—exiled from public life and discourse.

Terry Gross, host of Fresh Air, asked Dr. Bernard Lewis, Professor Emeritus of Near Eastern Studies at Princeton University, why the Muslim world seemed so "backward" in terms of women's rights and treatment. He quoted a Turkish writer who pondered the same question in 1848: "We are backward compared to the West because we deprive ourselves of the talents and abilities of half our population. We are impoverished by the incapacitation of women. We are as handicapped as a human body paralyzed on one side."

Imagine the churches, synagogues, and mosques of the world reading the story of the Divine Girl-Child whose birth was announced and celebrated by angels, whose coming merited visitors and precious gifts, and in whose honor the peoples of the world gather for a yearly retelling of the story of her birth. Imagine this story being read from Bible, Koran, and Torah:

In this hour everything is stillness. There is total silence and awe. We are overwhelmed with a great wonder. We keep vigil. We are expecting the coming of the Divine Girl-Child.

In the fullness of time, she is born. She shines like the sun, bright and beautiful. She is laughing a most joyful laugh. She is a delight, soothing the world with peace.

Become bold. Lean over and look at her. Touch her face. Lift her in your hands with great awe. Look at her more closely. There is no blemish on her. She is splendid to see.

She opens her eyes and looks intently at you. A powerful light comes forth from her eyes, like a flash of lightning. The light of her gaze invites: The hidden one to come into the light. The sleeping one to awaken. The frozen one to thaw. The buried one to emerge. The hard and protected one to soften. Receive her healing gaze deep within your being.

Suddenly there appears a multitude of heavenly beings singing:
"Glory to the Mother of All Living and to her Daughter.
She has arrived. The Divine Child is among us.
She will bring peace and inspire goodwill among all people.

"Welcome her joyfully. Shout with a loud voice:
You belong here among us. We're glad you're alive!
Surround her with goodness, safety, and laughter.
She is the Divine Child, come among us this day."

May the nations of the world and its religious communities celebrate the girl-child's birth with as much pomp, circumstance, and opportunity as her brother's; honor her body and natural processes without shame and violence; and allow her equal access to its pulpits and altars, thrones, boardrooms, and negotiating tables. As it was in the very beginning, may it be now, for the salvation of our world.

Lilith, the Rebellious First Woman

I am Lilith. My story is unknown to most of you. It was excluded from the Scripture. Yet it is a stubborn story, surviving on the margins of religious history. I am Lilith, the rebellious first woman. I will tell my own story. I will reclaim my former glory.

In the very beginning there was Darkness. It flamed forth in power. It asserted itself and I was created. In the image of the Moon was I brought forth. I reached toward the Depths. In the very beginning there was Light. It flamed forth in radiance. It asserted itself and the Sun was created. It reached toward the Heights. Darkness and Light were equal in dignity. Moon and Sun shone equal in splendor. Depth and Height were held equal in respect.

In the beginning there was a dispute. The Light feared the Darkness and its power. The Sun feared the Moon and its night. The Heights feared the Depths and its unknown. The Light swallowed the Darkness. The Sun swallowed the Moon. The Heights swallowed the Depths. The old ways were almost forgotten. New stories were told.

According to the rabbis, the Breath of Life and the Dust of Earth formed me and Adam. We were created from the same source, so I expected full equality with him. He did not agree with me on that and other matters. He demanded that I serve him and that I lie beneath him when we made love. I was outraged. With the help of "The Name That Is Not to Be Spoken," I flew away. I vanished into thin air and settled at the Red Sea. Adam complained to God, who sent three angels after me. Their attempts to capture me were fruitless. I preferred living alone to life with the man.

My story is very simple. Remembering my former glory before I was swallowed into the rabbis' commentary, I refused to be mistreated by man or God. I did what any self-respecting woman would have done. I said, "Enough is enough," and I left! But you should hear the names they have called me and the stories they have told about me over the centuries.

They call me Spinster because I live alone and am perfectly content. I refuse to allow men to hold me in check. This they cannot understand so I am called Spinster.

They call me Night Hag, not to be confused with ugly, mind you. Some thought my daughters and me so beautiful and so expert at lovemaking that after an experience with us, a man was never again satisfied with mortal women.

They call me Whore, Harlot, and Seducer. Celibate monks tried to keep me away by sleeping with their hands over their genitals, clutching a crucifix. Men say I distract them from their progress toward personal salvation. Eve is the wife, the faithful woman. I am a seducer.

They call me Tormentor of Men. Although my story disappeared from the Bible, my daughters, the Lilim, are said to have haunted men for thousands of years. Well into the Middle Ages, Jewish men were manufacturing magic charms to keep away the Lilim. We supposedly appear at night and exert magical powers over young men. They said we caused their nocturnal emissions.

All that I represent threatens them, so they call me names. They call my refusal to be submissive and subordinate, rebelliousness. They call my assertiveness in taking care of myself, bitchiness. They call my independence of men, unfeminine. They call my sexuality, unconnected to a husband, unnatural. I am tired of their names!

Woman, is it any wonder you, too, have feared me? They have convinced you that all I represent is evil, unnatural, and unfeminine. Is it any wonder that you exile me from within you?

Mother Darkness

Gathering in the Darkness

CRONE MOTHER:

> We are gathered to honor the darkness.
> Come, let us settle into the darkness.

Settling into the Darkness

READER:

> Mother Darkness invites you
> to settle into your seat in this dark room,
> surrounded by the dark night,
> supported by the dark earth beneath you.
>
> Enter into the darkness of this space;
> feel the dark night surrounding you;
> touch the dark earth under your feet.
> Settle into your seat and breathe.

READER:

> Mother Darkness invites you
> to settle into your breath,
> moving in and through and around you
> in its own invisibility, in its own darkness.
>
> Linger with your breath in the silent darkness.
> Feel it move into the darkness around you
> and then return, always returning, to the darkness
> within you. Settle into your breath and breathe.

READER:

> Mother Darkness invites you
> to settle into your body, conceived in darkness,
> formed in darkness, thrust from the darkness.
>
> Linger a while with your body.
> Feel it, present and still,

held by the darkness surrounding you.
Settle into your body and breathe.

READER:

Mother Darkness invites you
to settle into the darkness within you
the deep dark, the quiet dark, the empty dark,
under-the-covers dark, eyes-closed-tight dark,
underground dark, womb dark.

Enter into the silent, empty, underground,
womb dark. Linger a while in the darkness.
Settle into the darkness and breathe.

Sharing in the Darkness

CRONE MOTHER:

In the very beginning was the Dark,
swirling with full-emptiness
vast with mystery and possibility.

The Dark desired,
she longed to bring something forth
to push something from her full emptiness,
to thrust something from her vast mysterious possibility.

Ask the quiet deep darkness within you:
What do you long to bring forth
to thrust forward, to push out,
to end, to begin, to change?
In the company of your friends and loved ones,
share aloud your wishes, dreams, desires, and longings.

ALL:

In wisdom, we acknowledge that everything changes. In the fullness of time, the hidden wish comes into the light, the sleeping dream awakens, the frozen desire thaws, the hard and protected longing softens. We wait in hope.

The Maternal Deep

The well was a holy place to our earliest ancestors—a passageway to the underground womb, the maternal deep. While visiting the well, they prayed to the well's resident goddess, asking her to meet their heart's desire. Imagine a well of living water within you.

Gaze into the well and see Eve, The Mother of All Living. Her womb waters offer you ongoing rebirth and transformation. She looks upon you with mercy and lovingkindness. Her eyes remind you of your original goodness. Reach into the waters as a prayer to The Mother of All Living:

Source of Life, to you I come.
Welcoming is your womb. Nurturing is your love.
In you I am enclosed and sustained.
With your womb-waters, bless the fertile ground of my goodness.

Gaze into the well and see Mary, The Queen of Heaven, within you. From her breasts flow fountains of living water. Drink of her living water, moistening the ground of creativity within you, calling forth the fruit of your creative womb. Reach into the waters as a prayer to The Queen of Heaven:

Hail, Mary, full of grace. I am one with you.
Blessed art thou among all living.
And blessed are the creative fruits of your Virginity,
springing forth in new images and new life.
With your womb-waters, bless the fertile ground of my creativity.

Gaze again into the well and see Lilith, The Rebellious First Mother. She looks upon you with strength. Her eyes remind you of your original courage and power. From her maternal deep, you are born again unto self-possession and self-respect. Reach into the waters as a prayer to The Rebellious First Mother:

Source of Life, From you I am pushed.
Strong is your womb. Powerful its thrust.
In you I exert, initiate, and move.
With your womb-waters, bless the fertile ground of my strength.

Gaze into the well and see your own mother. She held and nurtured you within her. In the fullness of time, she pushed you from her. All that she gave birth to is good, it is very good. Across the distance born of anger and of love, reach into the waters as a prayer to your mother:

Mother, I will free your voice to shout out the pain of a lifetime.
Your silence is mine. My voice is yours.
Your pain is mine. My healing is yours.
Together we will speak and heal the pain of a lifetime.
With your womb-waters, bless the fertile ground of my wholeness.

Go from here confident in your goodness, joyful in your creativity, and sustained by your strength. You are blessed by the Mother. And so it is.

Ceremony of Self-Commitment

A Call to Gather

Open your eyes and look around you. We have chosen the forest as our cathedral. We have invited the tall ancient redwoods as honored guests. We have invited the inhabitants of the forest to be among us. We have invited the moist, green growing things to bless us. We have gathered to witness each woman's vow of faithfulness. Be present in this place.

Open your heart and look within you. Breathe into this moment and release all distractions: Excursions into the past, projections into the future. Breathing in, receive the fullness of this moment. Breathing out, open to the gift and challenge of this moment. We are gathered to witness each woman's vow of faithfulness. Be present here and now.

An Invocation of Spirit

We invoke the presence of the Source of All Life. Everything in the forest comes from and returns to the Mother. You are as grounded, as connected to Her as the trees are. You are held, supported, and nourished by Her. Acknowledge the firm ground of the Mother holding you. Mother, we welcome you here.

We invoke the spirit of life, the breath. Everything breathes in the forest. Savor the breath of life, flowing in, through, and around you. Inhale deeply as the breath rises from the rich earth beneath you. Release the breath into the cool moist air around you. Breath, we welcome you here.

We invoke the wisdom of the body. Notice the ancient trees around you. You are one with the forest. Feel your feet grow roots extending deep into the ground. Feel your arms become branches stretching high in the sky. Sway with the breeze. Settle into your woman-body. Wise body, we welcome you here.

We invoke the accumulation of our years and experience. Notice the forest-dance of life and death and rebirth. Reach down and touch the forest floor layered with seasons passed. Look up and view the forest canopy woven from time's evolving. Acknowledge the seasons of your life. Invoke the richness of your years. Accumulation of years and experience, we welcome you here.

Musical Interlude

A Commitment

Daughter of Woman, in response to the truth, in love with yourself, full of boldness and grace, express your commitment with the words "I Will."

Will you love your body all the days of your life? Will you touch it with tenderness and support it with strength? Will you honor its rhythms and cycles as an exquisite resource? Will you honor the body of the goddess in your changing body?

Will you listen to the deep wisdom of your body all the days of your life? Will you meet its needs with tenderness and grace? Will you design the shape of your days in accordance with its feedback? Will you eat foods that support its vitality, drink water to moisten its capacities, and sleep well to renew its life energy?

Will you embrace your sexuality as your own all the days of your life? Will you delight in pleasuring yourself? Will you explore the edges of your sensuality? Will you trust your body's clear *yes* and *no* in the choice of lovers.

Will you honor the whole range of human emotion all the days of your life? Will you circulate your feelings daily, allowing them to pass through you as gracefully as the breath? Will you take responsibility for meeting your own emotional needs, enlisting the support of respectful friends and chosen family?

Will you speak your truth all the days of your life? Will you tell the untold truths of a lifetime to your parents, lovers, and colleagues, and to your children and grandchildren? Will you assume intellectual equality by refusing to defer to the thoughts and perceptions of others?

Will you love your creative impulses all the days of your life? Will you give expression daily to the words, shapes, images, and movements that emerge from within you? Will you celebrate your unique vision and experience, producing original creations and refusing to color inside someone else's lines?

Will you sustain interest in yourself all the days of your life? Will you embrace your own life as teacher, healer, and challenge? Will you value its lessons above the prescriptions of experts? Will you befriend the solitude of your own life?

Will you choose to be full of yourself all the days of your life? Will you honor your desire for acknowledgment and recognition? Will you surround yourself with friends who applaud your fullness?

Reading of the Vows
Let us witness each woman's vow of faithfulness. Let us review our commitment to ourselves as we listen. (The vows are spoken.)

Blessing of the Symbols
SPOKEN TO BLESS THE SYMBOLS: With holy water from the womb of the Mother, we bless each symbol. May it be a reminder of your vow when you forget yourself. May it escort you home when you wander away from yourself. May it bring a smile to your soul all the days of your life.

SPOKEN BY ALL THE WOMEN: As a sign of my love and respect for myself, I give myself this sacred symbol with a pledge to honor my vow in tender times and turbulent times. In graceful moments and in awkward situations. In flowing times and in seasons of stagnation. In fullness and in emptiness. In fear and in courage. In trouble and in beauty. With all that I am and all I shall become. For the rest of my life.

Musical Interlude

A Pronouncement of Loving Partnership
Inasmuch as you have grown in knowledge and love of yourself, and have vowed faithfulness to your life and capacities, I now joyfully proclaim it is right and good that you are woman. You are full of yourself!

A Blessing
SPOKEN BY ALL PARTICIPANTS IN UNISON:
No more waiting.
This is it. This is my life.
Nothing to wait for. Nowhere else to go.
No one to make it all different. This is it.
What a relief to have finally landed
Here. Now. Blessed be my life!

Adam and Eve Make Peace

The ultimate salvation of the world depends upon a coming together of the masculine and feminine, offering their combined strength, wisdom, and compassion in service of humankind. As each couple gathered here today finds their way to a sacred meeting place beyond right and wrong, beyond blaming and shaming, beyond one-up and one-down, the world becomes a safer, more sane place for all of us.

Hildegard of Bingen, the 12th century Benedictine abbess famed for her art and music, wrote, "All things in the world have been made in consideration of everything else. Everything in the heavens, on the earth, and under the earth, is penetrated with connectedness, with relatedness." Hildegard believed that the blessings of life came from this reservoir of oneness and the troubles of life were rooted in the belief in fragmentation and separation from this holistic Source.

Our socialization flows from separation-based beliefs in the inherent opposition, irreconcilable differences, and unbridgeable chasms between men and women. From childhood we were taught to gather evidence for how different we are from the "opposite sex." Men are from Mars. Women are from Venus.

Later in life, we seek a partner. For a while we suspend our separation-based beliefs. We gather evidence of our compatibility, of our shared experiences, visions, and dreams. Once the romantic dust settles, however, we return, by default, to the "story" of old. Soon the chasms deepen, the differences solidify, and "the battle between the sexes" intensifies.

In the name of the infinite wholeness, oneness, and relatedness of All That Is, acknowledged by every religious and spiritual tradition, I challenge you to gather evidence for your oneness, your similarity, your relatedness to each other; to reconcile all seeming differences, bridge all seeming chasms, and embrace all seeming opposites within your experience.

You are *one*. As you love yourself, you love your partner. As you forgive yourself, you forgive your partner. You are *one* body, breathing the same breath. You are *one* mind, thinking the same thoughts. You are *one* essence, living from the same source. In the irresistible coming together of your bodies, hearts, and minds, you bestow the essence of love upon each other. In your sexual coming together, you receive each other again and again as a prayer, a passionate, whole and holy prayer, affirming the union of all that is.

The Incredible Fitness of Things

Last year I walked through downtown Oakland several times a week to volunteer at my church and the YWCA. At the intersection of 13th and 14th Streets I passed a triangular-shaped park. It is only big enough to hold one bench and a shade-offering hundred year old tree. Sitting on the bench was a man with four or five bulging plastic bags at his feet. Whenever I passed by, he was reading a book.

One day I walked into the park, sat on the bench, and introduced myself: "I'm Patricia. What books do you read day and night?" "Mysteries. Been reading since I was three," he answered. We shared the names of our favorite mystery writers. He refused to share his name. I asked if I could call him "Professor." He said yes. The next time I brought mysteries from my shelf. He accepted a couple of them. Several he had already read.

As I walked away from him that day, I planned a rescue-mission: I'll mobilize the church to support him...surely someone has an extra bedroom, we'll provide a doctor to tend to his eyes, regular meals, canvas satchels to replace his garbage bags. In the midst of my savior-fantasies, a loud *no* rose from the depths of me with these words: "Do not seek to possess this child of life. His journey is sacred. Do not judge or tamper with it. Simply receive him as you would a beautiful iris in the garden of life. Relax in his presence and enjoy him."

I told the Professor about my rescue-fantasies. He said, "Why would I want the life of those who rush by this park every day? Only one in a hundred seems satisfied, quiet inside. I'm content to read. I sleep under the eaves in back of the library. They leave books for me there. I find the food I need each day." We continued our book exchanges and discussions about life's meaning. I went away for two months in the summer and when I returned I walked to the park to find the professor. He wasn't there. I asked folks in the buildings adjacent to the park about him but no one had seen him for weeks.

Just as the irises in my neighbor's yard bless my vision for a few months each year, our friendship was for a season. In his company I let go of my "savior-complex" and enjoyed the incredible beauty of the life he had chosen. The Professor taught me to honor the "fitness of things as they are." Turning toward him this day, I am reminded of these words from Alan Watts' book of essays *This Is It*:

"*This is it. To the individual thus enlightened it appears as a vivid and overwhelming certainty that the universe, precisely as it is at this moment, as a whole and in every one of its parts, is so completely right as to need no explanation or justification beyond what it simply is.*

The mind is so wonderstruck at the self-evident and self-sufficient fitness of things as they are, including what would ordinarily be thought the very worst, that it cannot express the perfection and beauty of the experience. The central core of this experience of life seems to be the conviction, or insight, that the immediate now, whatever its nature, is the goal and fulfillment of all living."

∴ ABOUT THE AUTHOR

A graduate of Princeton Theological Seminary, Patricia Lynn Reilly conducts spirituality, creativity, and self-esteem retreats; lectures widely; publishes inspirational books and resources; and manages two web sites: www.OpenWindowGallery.com, featuring the artists she enjoys, and www.OpenWindowCreations.com, featuring the books and resources she writes. Inspired by her daily walks around Lake Merritt, the jewel in the center of urban Oakland, California, Patricia honors the beauty of life through her photography, images, and writing. She is the author of four popular books of non-fiction.

∴ **OPEN WINDOW CREATIONS**
Life-Affirming Books, Resources, and Events

A Word From Patricia
Open Window Creations began as an intuitive impulse. While designing a flyer to describe my work, I searched for a name and image capable of holding the full range of my creative adventures: from workshop facilitation, event production, and resource design, to writing books and performing sacred dramas. The name "Open Window Creations" came to my awareness along with a poem-prayer: "Blow, fresh air, blow...into dusty rooms of old. Refresh and make new."

The importance of the open window image reaches into my childhood. I desperately longed for an open window, a breath of fresh air, a reminder of the world beyond the four-walls of the children's shelter, the orphanage, and the violent alcoholic homes of early childhood. Having healed into the present, I now use my creativity to blow fresh insight and understanding into dusty rooms of long-held, yet unexamined, theological, psychological, and personal beliefs.

Companion Resources
Patricia offers a variety of workshops, retreats, services, and presentations for women and men based on the writings included in *Words Made Flesh*. Contact www.wordsmadeflesh.com for the details of her speaking and workshop schedule. Patricia's current topics include:

Conscious Relationship
    A Matching Yes
    Happiness to Thy Sheets
    Adam and Eve Make Peace
Conscious Living
    The Circle of Life
    In the Fullness of Time
    The Incredible Fitness of Things
Conscious Parenting
    Outrageous Words
    Remember Your WOW-ness
    Something Old, Something New
Conscious Spirituality
    A Free Imagination
    Moving Beyond Gender
    The Unbeliever's Guide to Spirituality

Contact Open Window Creations

Visit www.openwindowcreations.com to review and purchase Patricia's books, posters, and poem-postcards, and to explore and register for OWC's transformational events, presentations, and intensives. Visit www.openwindowgallery.com to enjoy the creativity of some of Patricia's favorite artists. Add your name to OWC's e-mail list and you will receive inspirational e-reflections. Add your name to OWC's snail-mail list and you will receive quarterly newsletters, announcing regional events.

Open Window Creations
    P. O. Box 8615
    Berkeley, California 94707
    info@openwindowcreations.com
    www.openwindowcreations.com
    www.openwindowgallery.com

∴ PATRICIA LYNN REILLY'S BOOKS

Available from Open Window Creations and local bookstores.

A God Who Looks Like Me:
Discovering a Woman-Affirming Spirituality
Supports you to design a personal spirituality by extending your historical, theological, and personal vision to include the divine feminine. A richly woven tapestry of ritual, story, and history gently encouraging you to exorcise old images and to embrace woman-affirming ones. (BALLANTINE BOOKS, 1995)

Be Full of Yourself!:
The Journey from Self-Criticism to Self-Celebration
Dismantles the self-critical question "what's wrong with me" by exploring its historical, theological, and personal origins. An invitation to descend into the richness of your own life and to learn the language of self-celebration.
(OPEN WINDOW CREATIONS, 1998)

Imagine a Woman in Love with Herself:
Embracing Your Wholeness and Wisdom
Explores twenty self-affirming qualities, encouraging you to grow in knowledge and love of yourself. Each stanza of the poem"Imagine a Woman" is followed by inspirational reflections and meditations. (CONARI PRESS, 1999)

I Promise Myself:
Making a Commitment to Yourself and Your Dreams
Refashions the wedding vow and ceremony into a transformational resource for women of all ages. Provides step by step guidelines for composing your own personal vow of faithfulness and creating a ceremony of commitment.
(CONARI PRESS, 2000)